Anatomy Student's Color-In Handbook

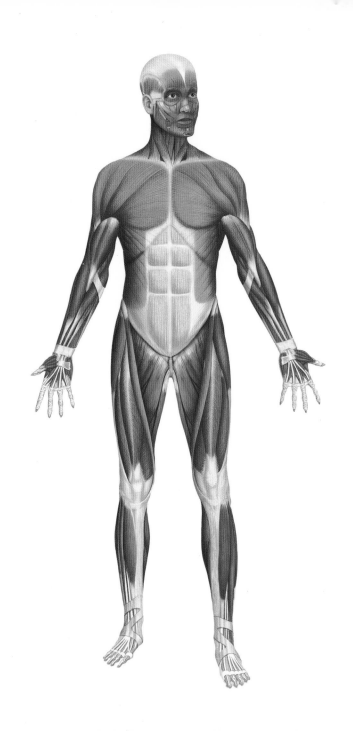

Anatomy Student's Color-In Handbook

VOLUME TWO:

Muscular System • Digestive System

Professor Ken Ashwell, BMedSc, MBBS, PhD

Quarto is the authority on a wide range of topics.

Quarto educates, entertains and enriches the lives of our readers—enthusiasts and lovers of hands-on living.

www.QuartoKnows.com

First published in 2017 by
Global Book Publishing Pty Ltd
Part of The Quarto Group
Level One, Ovest House,
58 West Street, Brighton, BN1 2RA, UK

ISBN: 978-0-85762-513-7

A Global Book

© 2017 Quarto Publishing PLC, 6 Blundell Street, London N7 9BH, UK

Printed and bound in China

Conceived, designed and produced by Global Book Publishing

Consultant Editor: Professor Ken Ashwell, BMedSc, MBBS, PhD

Designer: Angela English

Project Editor: Kathleen Steeden

Illustrations:
Joanna Culley, BA(Hons) RMIP, MMAA, IMI (Medical-Artist.com), Mike Gorman, Thomson Digital, Glen Vause

Contributors:
Robin Arnold, MSc, Ken Ashwell, BMedSc, MB, BS, PhD, Deborah Bryce, BSc, MScQual, MChiro, GrCertHEd, John Gallo, MB, BS(Hons), FRACP, FRCPA, Rakesh Kumar, MB, BS, PhD, Peter Lavelle, MB, BS, Karen McGhee, BSc, Michael Roberts, MB, BS, LLB(Hons), Emeritus Professor Frederick Rost, BSc(Med), MB, BS, PhD, DCP(London), DipRMS, Elizabeth Tancred, BSc, PhD, Dzung Vu, MD, MB, BS, DipAnat, GradCertHEd, Phil Waite, BSc(Hons), MBChB, CertHEd, PhD

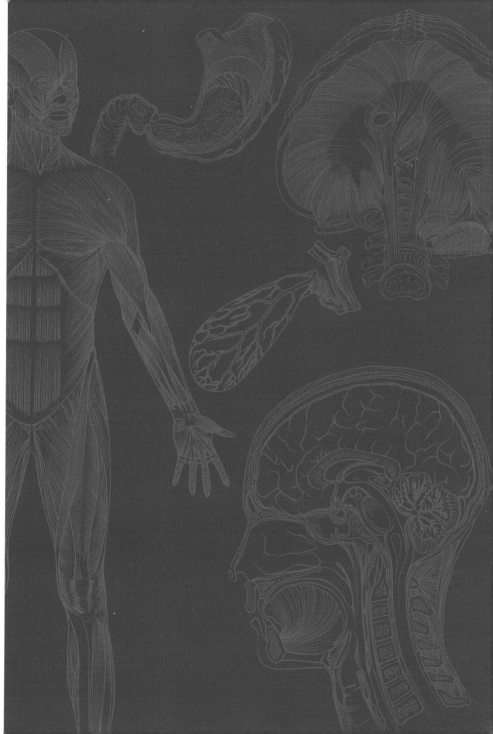

Contents

Digestive System

Introduction

There are two important principles embodied in this book. The first is that anatomy is a three-dimensional, fundamentally visual subject, which is best learned by the student using their hand and eye to follow the position, contours, and courses of bones, muscles, vessels, and nerves. Anatomy cannot be learned simply as textual information—for proper understanding of the structure of the human body, students must be able to hold the positions, relationships, and trajectories of anatomical structures in their "mind's eye."

The second is that learning in any field, but especially in anatomy, is most effective when it is an active process. Retention of knowledge is more complete when the student is actively involved in testing themselves against the body of knowledge they wish to retain. Passive immersion in a body of information by reading text will rarely lead to any significant retention of knowledge.

By combining these two important educational principles, this book provides an effective, convenient tool for students to master the important elements of human structure. Students are encouraged to use the book in conjunction with their recommended text to absorb and reinforce critically important concepts in the topography of the human body.

Ken Ashwell, BMedSc, MB, BS, PhD
Professor of Anatomy,
Department of Anatomy,
School of Medical Sciences,
The University of New South Wales
Sydney, Australia

This book is designed to assist students and professionals to identify body parts and structures, and the numbered leader lines aid the process by clearly pointing out each body part. The function of coloring allows you to familiarize yourself with individual parts of the body and check your knowledge.

Coloring is best done using either pencils or pens in a variety of dark and light colors. Where possible, you should use the same color for like structures, so that all completed illustrations can be utilized later as visual references. According to anatomical convention, the color green is usually reserved for lymphatic structures, yellow for nerves, red for arteries, and blue for veins.

The numbered leader lines that point to separate parts of the illustration enable you to consolidate and then check your knowledge using the keys and descriptions on the facing page.

Muscular System

Muscle cells produce movement but also provide protective walls for body cavities, support internal organs, and help regulate the internal environment. Muscle cells are of three types: skeletal, cardiac, and smooth. Skeletal muscle has at least one attachment to bone and is under voluntary control. It is responsible for all limb and trunk movement, chewing and swallowing, facial expression, and breathing. Cardiac muscle is the involuntary muscle of the heart that beats continuously from embryonic life to death. Smooth muscle cells fill the walls of internal organs and blood vessels, acting without voluntary control to maintain a constant internal environment.

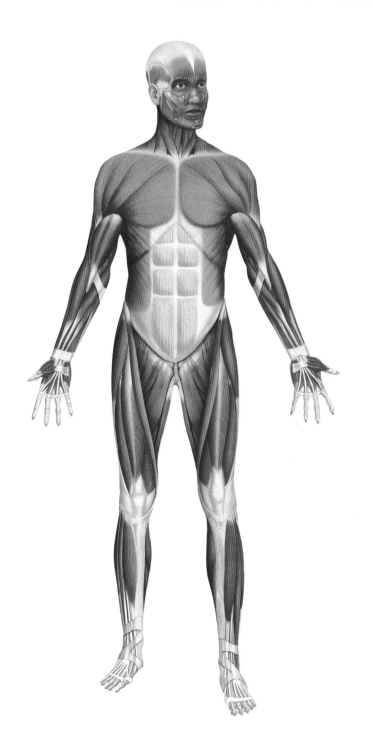

Muscular System

Key:

1 Temporalis
2 Masseter
3 Sternohyoid
4 Sternocleidomastoid
5 Pectoralis major
6 Serratus anterior
7 External abdominal oblique
8 Brachioradialis
9 Iliopsoas
10 Pectineus
11 Adductor longus
12 Flexor carpi radialis

13 Flexor digitorum superficialis
14 Flexor carpi ulnaris
15 Rectus abdominis .
16 Triceps brachii
17 Brachialis
18 Biceps brachii
19 Deltoid
20 Trapezius
21 Orbicularis oris
22 Orbicularis oculi
23 Frontalis

Description:

The muscular system, which brings about body movement, includes the voluntary muscles of the body. There are about 700 muscles in the human body, and they vary greatly in size—from tiny muscles that wrinkle the forehead to large muscles in the thigh. Muscle fibers attach either directly to a bone or to a tendon that is fixed to a bone. The force produced by the contraction of muscle fibers is transmitted to the bone by the tendon.

Continued on page 14

anterior view

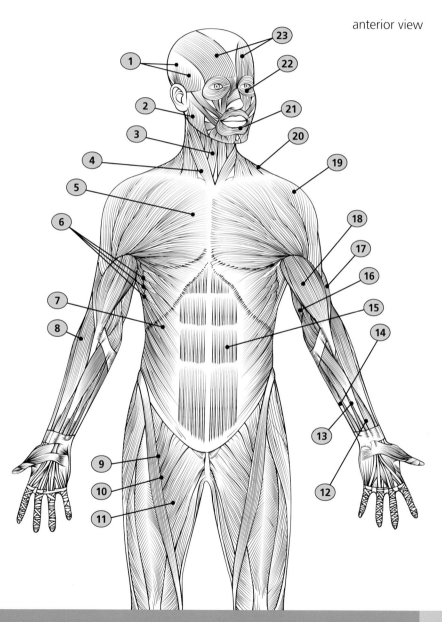

Muscular System

Key:

1 Adductor magnus
2 Sartorius
3 Gastrocnemius
4 Soleus
5 Extensor hallucis longus tendon
6 Extensor digitorum longus
7 Tibialis anterior
8 Quadriceps femoris (3 of the 4 heads)
9 Tensor fasciae latae

Description:

Continued from page 12

The action of a muscle depends on its position in relation to the joint it works on. Each movement of a limb, however simple, is the result of a number of muscles working together. Usually a muscle contracts when it is activated, and if the force of a muscle contraction is greater than the force that is resisting the contraction, the contraction is isotonic. If the resistance to contraction is equal to the force generated in muscle tissues, the muscle will not shorten, and this is called an isometric contraction.

anterior view

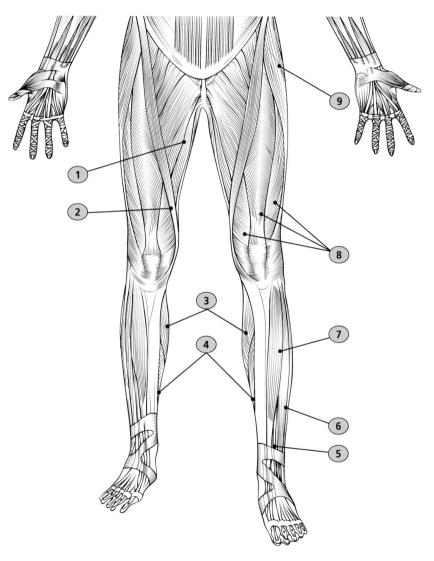

Muscular System

Key:

1	Occipitalis	9	Abductor pollicis longus
2	Trapezius	10	Extensor digitorum
3	Deltoid	11	Brachioradialis
4	Latissimus dorsi	12	Triceps brachii
5	External abdominal oblique	13	Teres major
6	Flexor carpi ulnaris	14	Teres minor
7	Gluteus maximus	15	Sternocleidomastoid
8	Extensor pollicis brevis	16	Temporalis

Description:

Skeletal muscle is the most prominent type of muscle in the body and may account for up to 60 percent of the mass of the body. It is usually attached to the bones of the skeleton at both ends by tendons. Skeletal muscle is under conscious control and is therefore called voluntary muscle.

Continued on page 18

posterior view

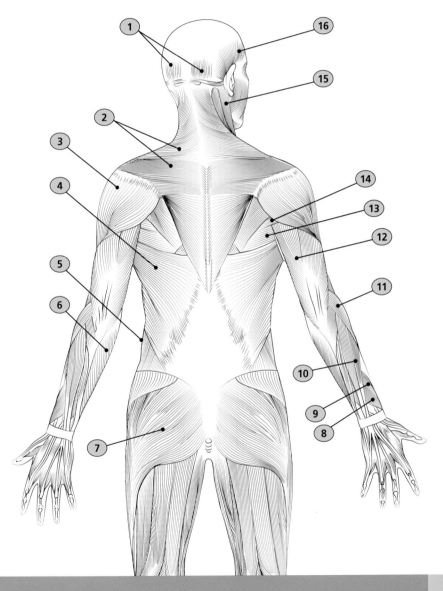

Muscular System

Key:

1 Vastus lateralis
2 Gastrocnemius, medial head
3 Soleus
4 Adductor magnus
5 Gracilis
6 Achilles tendon
7 Fibularis longus
8 Semimembranosus
9 Semitendinosus
10 Long head of biceps femoris

Description:

Continued from page 16

Some skeletal muscles are visible beneath the skin's surface and are responsible, along with the skeleton, for an individual's physique.

posterior view

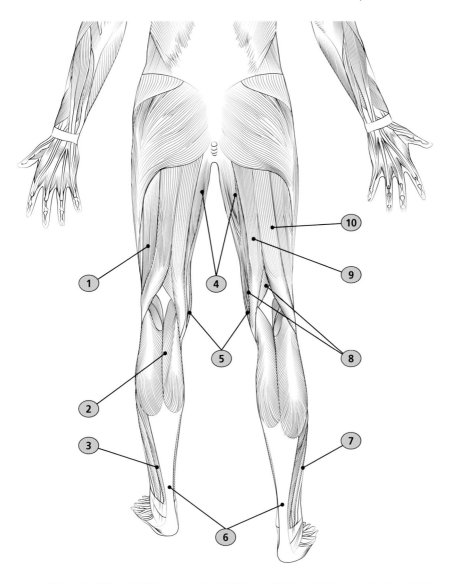

Muscle Fiber

Key:

1 Sarcoplasmic reticulum
2 Transverse tubules
3 Sarcomere
4 Myofibril
5 Myosin
6 Actin
7 Myosin head

8 Myosin crossbridge
9 Actin
10 Myosin tail
11 Muscle fiber
12 Myofibril
13 Nuclei

Description:
Muscle fibers are elongated cells containing myofibrils. Each myofibril is made up of thousands of overlapping thin actin filaments and thicker myosin filaments. Where actin and myosin filaments overlap, they are linked by connections (crossbridges) that participate in muscle shortening (contraction).

microstructure

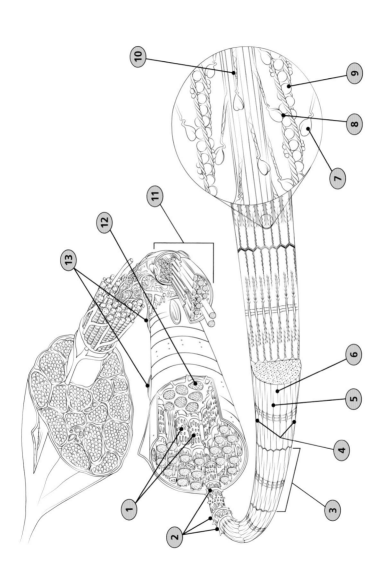

Muscle Types

Key:

1 Unipennate
2 Bipennate
3 Multipennate
4 Spiral
5 Radial
6 Quadrate
7 Strap

Description:

Muscles are classified based on their general shape—some muscles have mainly parallel fibers, and others have oblique fibers. The shape and arrangement of muscle fibers reflect the function of the muscle. The pennate muscles have a featherlike appearance, and their fibers run obliquely down to the tendon. Some spiral muscles have the capacity to turn half a rotation between their attachments, while others twist around a bone.

Continued on page 24

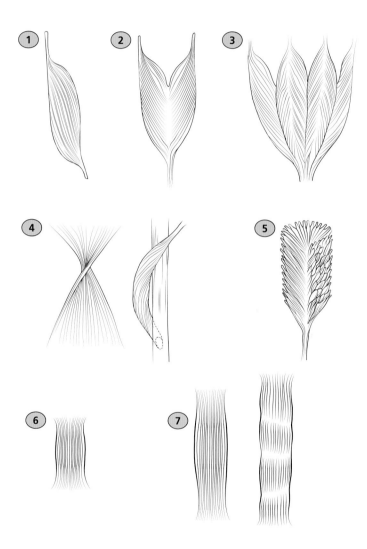

Muscle Types

Key:

1 Cruciate
2 Triangular
3 Multicaudal
4 Fusiform
5 Digastric
6 Circular (sphincteric)
7 Bicipital
8 Tricipital
9 Quadricipital

Description:

Continued from page 22

Muscles consist of bundles of fibers that can be organized in different ways, according to the function of the muscle. Muscle fibers attach either directly to a bone or to a tendon that is fixed to a bone. The force exerted by a muscle depends on its cross-sectional area, whereas the distance that a muscle can shorten depends on its relaxed length. In the common spindle-shaped muscles, all muscle fibers run from one tendon to another. In the case of the circular muscles, the fibers are arranged in concentric circles.

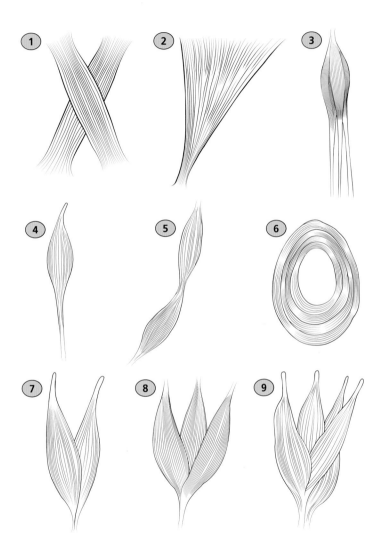

Superficial and Deep Muscles of the Head and Neck

Key:

1 Temporalis

2 Masseter

3 Scalenus anterior

4 Scalenus medius

5 Levator scapulae

6 Trapezius (cut)

7 Trapezius

8 Sternocleidomastoid

9 Sternohyoid

10 Frontalis

Description:

The muscles covering the scalp region are collectively known as the epicranial muscles and include the occipitalis, frontalis, and temporoparietal muscles. The neck muscles attach to the front, back, and sides of the vertebrae, producing forward, backward, and sideways movements. Those with an oblique orientation also produce rotation (turning). The largest musculature lies to the back. Some of these muscles are exclusively related to moving the head and neck (splenius capitis and cervicis, and semispinalis capitis and cervicis), while others are related to moving the shoulder (trapezius, levator scapulae) or raising the upper two ribs (scalene muscles).

anterior view

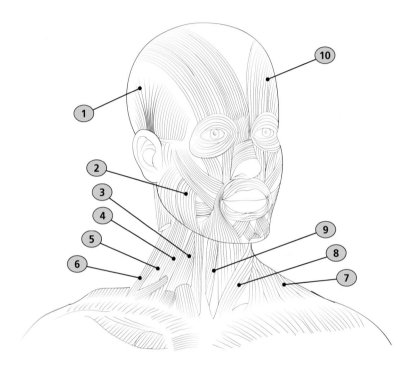

Superficial Muscles of the Head and Neck and Muscles of Facial Expression

Key:

1 Occipitalis
2 Splenius capitis
3 Levator scapulae
4 Scalenus posterior
5 Trapezius
6 Scalenus anterior
7 Scalenus medius
8 Sternocleidomastoid
9 Depressor anguli oris
10 Buccinator
11 Zygomaticus major
12 Zygomaticus minor
13 Levator labii superioris
14 Levator labii superioris alaeque nasi
15 Orbicularis oculi
16 Frontalis
17 Galea aponeurotica

Description:

The occipital and frontalis muscles perform several actions. The occipital part of the epicranial muscles acts to draw the scalp backward, while the frontalis part acts to raise the eyebrows. The splenius capitis moves the head backward. The levator scapulae and trapezius muscles work to raise and rotate the scapula. The three scalene muscles raise the ribs and flex the neck. The sternocleidomastoid acts to rotate the head.

The muscles of facial expression work in unison to create a number of different facial movements. Some muscles of the eye region are regulated by the autonomic nervous system. The muscles of the mouth are used in speech and digestive processes, as well as in expression. Zygomaticus minor and major pull the corners of the mouth upward and outward. Depressor anguli oris pulls the corners of the mouth downward. Buccinator compresses the cheeks. Levator labii superioris raises the upper lip. Levator labii superioris alaeque nasi raises the upper lip and dilates the nostrils. Orbicularis oculi closes the eyelids.

lateral view

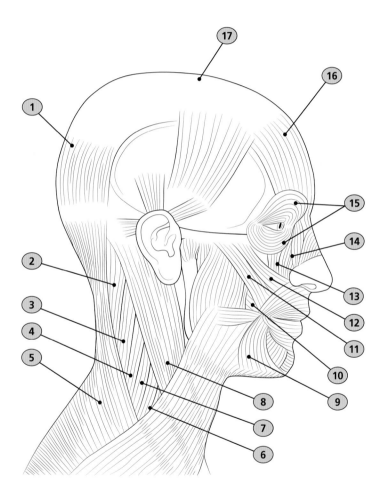

Deep Muscles of the Head and Neck

Key:

1 Semispinalis capitis
2 Splenius capitis
3 Levator scapulae
4 Scalenus anterior
5 Scalenus medius
6 Scalenus posterior
7 Omohyoid (inferior belly)
8 Sternohyoid

9 Omohyoid (superior belly)
10 Thyrohyoid
11 Digastric (anterior belly)
12 Digastric (posterior belly)
13 Medial pterygoid
14 Lateral pterygoid
15 Temporalis

Description:

The largest musculature lies to the back of the head and neck. Some of these muscles are exclusively related to moving the head and neck (splenius capitis, splenius cervicis, semispinalis capitis, and semispinalis cervicis), while others are related to moving the shoulder (trapezius, levator scapulae) or raising the upper two ribs (scalene muscles).

The deep muscles of the jaw (the medial pterygoid and the lateral pterygoid) permit a wide range of movements to the movable lower jaw (mandible). Together, the medial pterygoid muscles act to raise the mandible (close the jaw). Alternating action of the two medial pterygoid muscles causes a grinding motion of the jaw. Acting together, the lateral pterygoid muscles protrude the mandible. Alternating action of both lateral pterygoid muscles produces side-to-side movement of the mandible.

lateral view

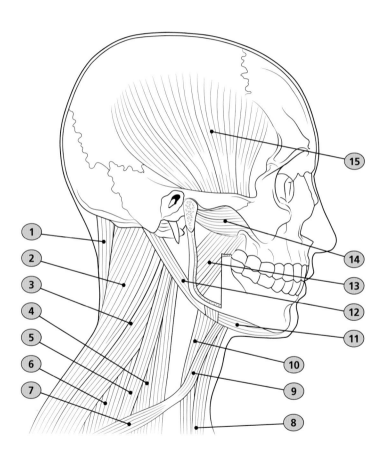

Muscular System

Muscles of the Eye

Key:

1 Trochlea
2 Lacrimal gland
3 Optic nerve
4 Inferior oblique
5 Inferior rectus
6 Lateral rectus (cut)
7 Medial rectus
8 Levator palpebrae superioris (cut)
9 Superior rectus
10 Superior oblique

Description:
The muscles of the eye (superior rectus, medial rectus, lateral rectus, inferior rectus, superior oblique, and inferior oblique) work in unison to offer a wide field of vision, by providing up, down, left, and right movement. These six muscles hold the eye suspended in the orbit of the skull. The six ocular muscles insert on the sclera.

Lateral rectus, superior rectus, medial rectus, and inferior rectus move the eye laterally, upward, medially, and downward, respectively. Superior oblique moves the eye downward and sideward. Inferior oblique moves the eye upward when the eye is turned medially.

lateral view—left eye

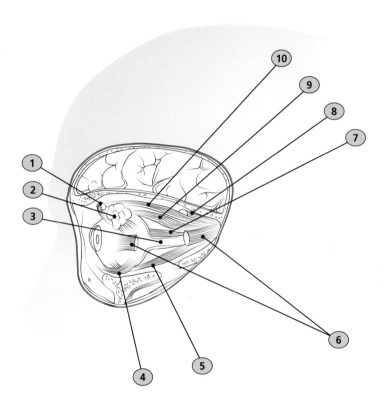

Muscles of the Eye

Key:

1 Lateral rectus
2 Superior rectus (cut)
3 Medial rectus
4 Superior oblique
5 Levator palpebrae superioris (cut on the right side)
6 Optic nerve

Description:

The movement of the eyeball is controlled by six muscles—superior rectus, medial rectus, lateral rectus, inferior rectus, superior oblique, and inferior oblique—which hold the eye suspended in the orbit of the skull, and allow the eye to look up, down, left, and right. Levator palpebrae superioris is involved in elevation of the upper eyelid. The six ocular muscles insert on the sclera.

Lateral rectus, superior rectus, medial rectus, and inferior rectus move the eye laterally, upward, medially, and downward, respectively. Superior oblique moves the eye downward and sideward. Inferior oblique elevates the eye when the eye has been turned medially by the medial rectus.

superior view

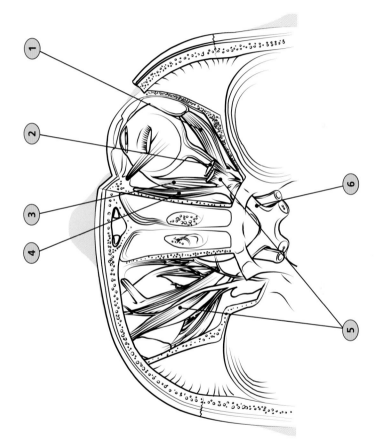

Superficial Muscles of the Jaw

Key:

1 Temporalis
2 Temporomandibular joint
3 Styloid process
4 Masseter
5 Mandible
6 Maxilla
7 Zygomatic bone

Description:

The superficial muscles of the jaw—the temporalis and the masseter—in combination with the deep muscles—the medial pterygoid and the lateral pterygoid—are the muscles of mastication. Combined, they allow the jaw to move up, down, to the side, forward, and backward. Both the temporalis and the masseter act to raise the mandible, thereby closing the jaw.

lateral view

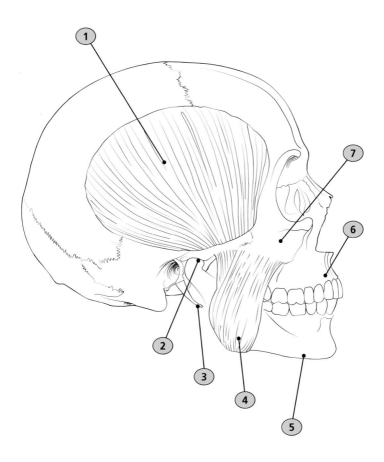

Deep Muscles of the Jaw

Key:

  1 Mandibular condyle
  2 Styloid process
  3 Lateral pterygoid
  4 Medial pterygoid
  5 Mandible
  6 Maxilla

Description:

The deep muscles of the jaw—the medial pterygoid and the lateral pterygoid—along with the superficial muscles—the masseter and the temporalis—permit a wide range of movements to the movable lower jaw (mandible). The jaw muscles are known as the muscles of mastication and also play a role in speech.

Together, the medial pterygoid muscles act to raise the mandible (close the jaw). Alternating action of the two medial pterygoid muscles causes a grinding motion of the jaw. Acting together, the lateral pterygoid muscles protrude the mandible. Alternating action of both lateral pterygoid muscles produces side-to-side movement of the mandible.

lateral view

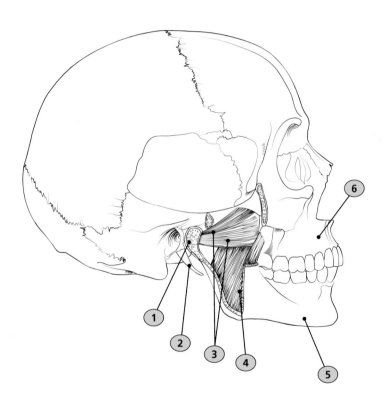

Muscles of the Pharynx

Key:
1 Stylopharyngeus
2 Inferior constrictor
3 Longitudinal muscle layer (of esophagus)
4 Circular muscle layer (of esophagus)
5 Middle constrictor
6 Superior constrictor

Description:
The constrictor muscles of the pharynx are involved in the digestive process, being responsible for moving food down to the esophagus. Named for the action they perform, the pharyngeal constrictor muscles constrict the pharynx. The stylopharyngeus and the deeper muscles (the palatopharyngeus and the salpingopharyngeus) are involved in elevating the pharynx.

posterior view

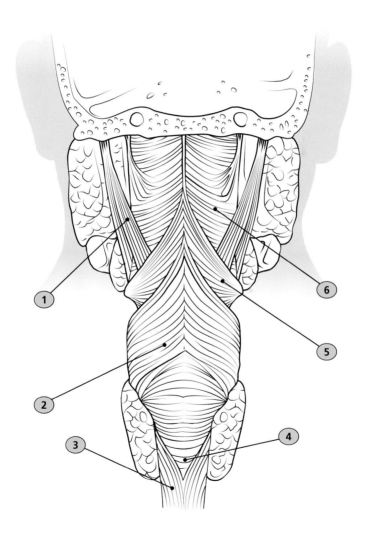

Muscles of the Neck

Key:

1 Cricothyroid
2 Sternocleidomastoid
3 Esophagus
4 Longus colli
5 Spinal cord
6 Levator scapulae
7 Trapezius
8 Scalenus medius
9 Scalenus anterior
10 Internal jugular vein
11 Common carotid artery
12 Thyroid

Description:

The transverse section of the neck shows the relationship among the components of the neck column. The neck can be divided into two major columns. At the back, the nuchal region includes the cervical vertebrae and their supporting musculature. In front, the neck includes a visceral column containing the larynx, trachea, pharynx, and esophagus.

The largest musculature lies to the back of the neck column. Some of these muscles are exclusively related to moving the head and neck, while others, such as the trapezius and levator scapulae, are related to moving the shoulder, or raising the upper two ribs (in the case of the scalene muscles).

transverse section

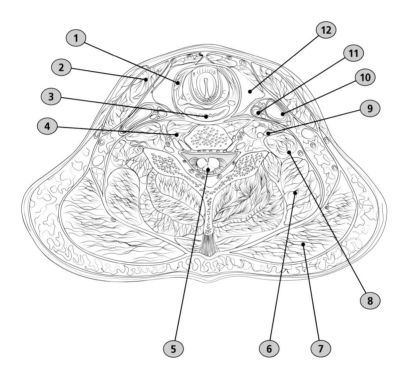

Superficial Muscles of the Back

Key:

1 Trapezius
2 Latissimus dorsi
3 External abdominal oblique
4 Thoracolumbar fascia

Description:

The superficial muscles of the back stabilize and move the scapula and humerus, and secondarily support the vertebral column. The extrinsic muscles of the back region include: the trapezius muscle, which extends from the neck and covers the upper back in a triangular shape, coming to a point at the midline; and latissimus dorsi, a fan-shaped sheet of muscle that extends from the vertebral column, tapering across to the humerus. The external abdominal oblique extends from the lower eight ribs down to the iliac crest.

While both the trapezius and latissimus dorsi cover much of the back region, their activities are centered around movement of the shoulder region and the humerus, respectively. The external abdominal oblique contributes to movement of the spine, participating in bending and flexing movements.

posterior view

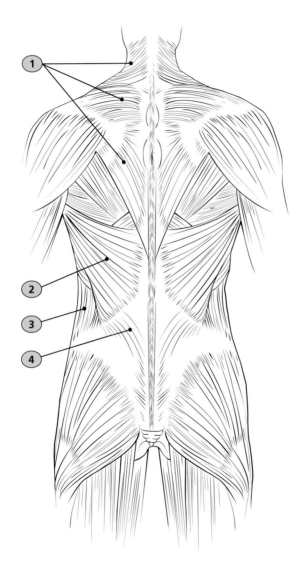

Intermediate and Deep Muscles of the Back

Key:

1 Semispinalis capitis
2 Rhomboid major
3 External intercostal muscles
4 Erector spinae
5 Serratus posterior inferior
6 Internal abdominal oblique
7 Sacrotuberous ligament
8 Multifidus
9 Quadratus lumborum

10 Semispinalis thoracis
11 Levatores costarum
12 Semispinalis cervicis
13 Scalenus posterior
14 Oblique capitis inferior
15 Rectus capitis posterior major
16 Rectus capitis posterior minor
17 Oblique capitis superior

Description:

The intermediate muscles of the back move the ribs and help respiration. Erector spinae is a large group of spinal extensor muscles that lie in layers of the back, from superficial to deep. Situated in the upper region of the back, semispinalis capitis is involved in head movement. The serratus posterior superior elevates the ribs, and the serratus posterior inferior pulls down the ribs. The external intercostal muscles elevate the thoracic cage. The internal abdominal oblique is involved in movement of the vertebral column.

Rectus capitis posterior minor and oblique capitis superior extend the head. Oblique capitis inferior helps to rotate the head. Rectus capitis posterior major extends and rotates the head. The scalenus posterior stabilizes and laterally flexes the neck. Semispinalis thoracis and semispinalis cervicis extend the thoracic and cervical areas of the vertebral column, and rotate the vertebral column. Rotatores and multifidus muscles extend and rotate the vertebral column. Quadratus lumborum presses down and stabilizes the twelfth rib.

posterior view

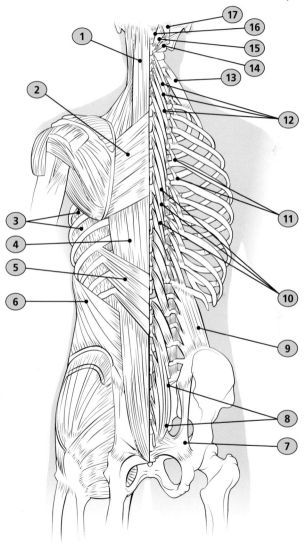

Superficial and Deep Muscles of the Thorax and Abdomen

Key:

1 Pectoralis minor
2 Internal intercostals
3 Latissimus dorsi
4 Internal abdominal oblique
5 Rectus abdominis
6 Transversus abdominis
7 External abdominal oblique
8 Serratus anterior
9 Pectoralis major

Description:

Superficial muscles of the thorax are the pectoralis major and serratus anterior. Supporting the abdominal organs, the abdominal wall is made up of sheetlike layers of muscles. The first superficial muscle of the abdomen is the external abdominal oblique. The deep muscles of the thorax and abdomen help in the breathing process and also provide support to the internal organs.

Pectoralis major is involved in various types of movements of the humerus. Serratus anterior is involved in shoulder movement, but also assists in moving the ribs during inhalation. The external abdominal oblique muscle compresses the abdomen. Pectoralis minor moves the shoulder and humerus. The internal intercostals depress the ribs. Latissimus dorsi adducts, extends, and medially rotates the humerus. The internal abdominal oblique and transversus abdominus compress the abdomen and help move the vertebral column. Rectus abdominis also compresses the abdomen and helps move the vertebral column.

anterior view

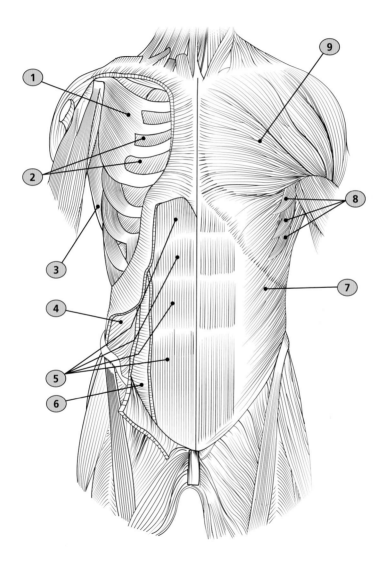

Muscles of the Posterior Wall of the Thoracic and Abdominal Cavities

Key:

   1 Innermost intercostal
   2 Diaphragm
   3 Levator ani (iliococcygeus and pubococcygeus)
   4 Piriformis
   5 Iliacus
   6 Psoas major
   7 Transversus abdominis
   8 Quadratus lumborum
   9 Mediastinal pleura

Description:

The muscles lining the wall of the thoracic and abdominal cavities provide body movement and support to the internal organs. The muscles of the thoracic cavity also assist in breathing. The innermost intercostal muscles lie deep to the internal intercostal muscles. The intercostal muscles span between the upper and lower borders of neighboring ribs.

anterior view

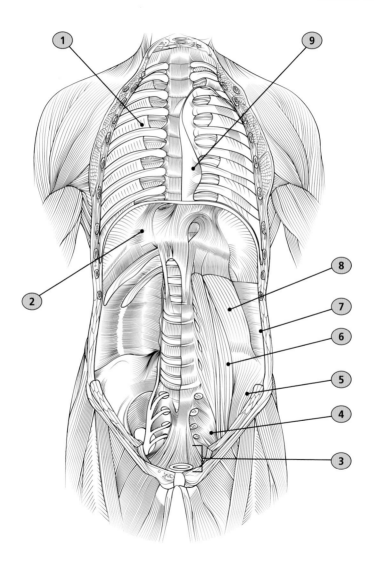

Intercostal and Other Chest Wall Muscles

Key:

1 Manubrium of sternum
2 Tenth rib
3 Internal intercostals
4 External intercostal
5 First rib
6 Clavicle

Description:

The intercostal muscles play an important role in breathing. The external intercostal muscles lie over the internal intercostal muscles. These two sets of muscles span between the upper and lower borders of neighboring ribs to form a complete unit. The external intercostal muscles act to elevate the ribs during inspiration. The internal intercostal muscles act to depress the ribs during expiration.

anterior view

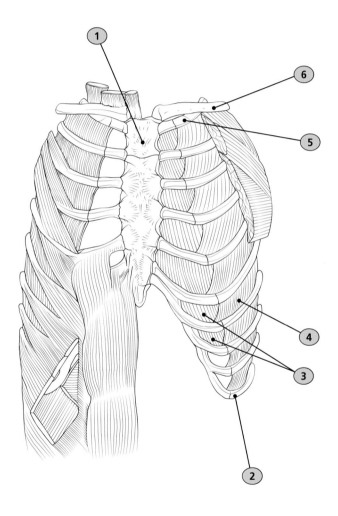

Diaphragm

Key:

1 Pericardium
2 Costal parietal pleura
3 Esophagus
4 Aorta
5 Body of a vertebra
6 Spinal cord
7 Azygos vein
8 Inferior vena cava
9 Diaphragmatic parietal pleura
10 Right phrenic nerve
11 Sternum
12 Central tendon of diaphragm

Description:

The diaphragm is a sheet of muscle that separates the chest cavity from the abdominal cavity. The diaphragm is the main muscle involved in inspiration. The heart and lungs lie on the upper convex surface of the diaphragm, with the pericardial sac, which surrounds the heart, firmly attached to the upper surface of the central tendon of the diaphragm. The diaphragm descends during inspiration, and, on relaxation, the muscle is pushed back up to its original position by the abdominal organs.

superior view

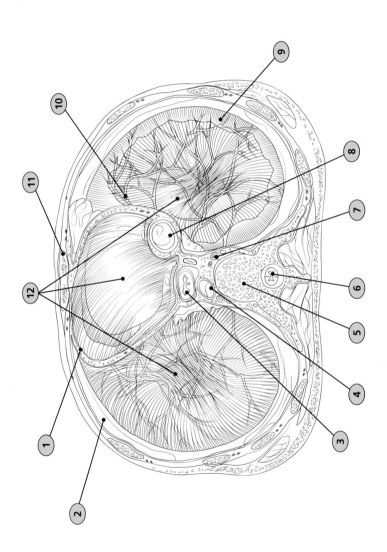

Diaphragm

Key:

1 Sternum
2 Central tendon of diaphragm
3 Inferior vena cava
4 Abdominal aorta
5 Right crus of diaphragm
6 Vertebral column
7 Left crus of diaphragm
8 Celiac trunk
9 Quadratus lumborum
10 Esophagus

Description:

The diaphragm is a muscular layer that separates the chest cavity from the abdominal cavity. The diaphragm is pierced by several structures that pass between the two cavities. The three largest of these structures are the esophagus, the aorta, and the inferior vena cava. The central part of the diaphragm is the central tendon, which is fibrous rather than muscular. The inferior surface of the diaphragm forms the roof of the abdominal cavity, and lies over the stomach and spleen on the left and the liver on the right.

At rest, the diaphragm forms a high dome; when the diaphragm contracts, the dome moves downward, thus increasing the height of the thoracic cavity, which results in air being drawn into the lungs. During expiration, the diaphragm relaxes, returning to its original position.

inferior view

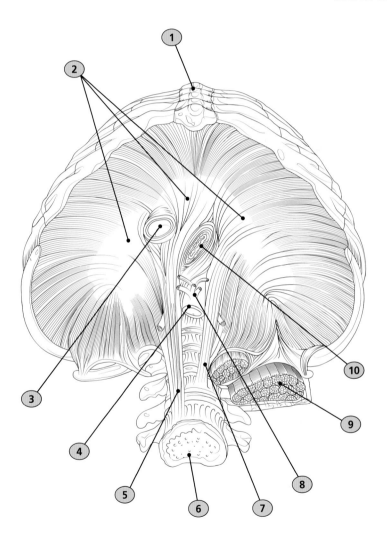

Pelvic Floor Muscles: Female

Key:

1 Lumbar vertebra (L5)
2 Sacral promontory
3 Piriformis
4 Ischiococcygeus (coccygeus)
5 Levator ani (iliococcygeus, pubococcygeus, and puborectalis)
6 Pubic symphysis
7 Urinary bladder
8 Vagina
9 Rectum
10 Obturator internus
11 Psoas major
12 Psoas minor
13 Anterior sacrococcygeal ligament

Description:

The pelvic floor muscles (pelvic diaphragm) support the abdominal organs. The pelvic floor is formed by the coccygeus and levator ani muscles, has a sphincteric action on the rectum and vagina, and assists in increasing intra-abdominal pressure. The puborectalis part of the pelvic diaphragm is important in fecal and urinary continence. The piriformis and obturator internus muscles form the pelvic walls.

The coccygeus acts to support the pelvic viscera and flex the coccyx. Levator ani acts to support the pelvic organs and to provide resistance to increases in intra-abdominal pressure.

superior view

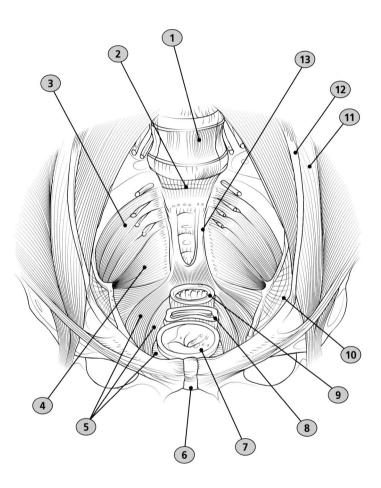

Muscles of the Perineum: Male

Key:

1 Ischiocavernosus
2 Bulbospongiosus
3 Deep transverse perineus (under urogenital diaphragm)
4 Superficial transverse perineus
5 Anus
6 Obturator internus
7 Coccygeus
8 Coccyx
9 Gluteus maximus
10 Iliococcygeus
11 Pubococcygeus
12 Ischial tuberosity
13 External anal sphincter
14 Midline raphe
15 Ramus of ischium
16 Penis

Description:

The perineum is a diamond-shaped "floor" at the base of the pelvis. It consists of a sheet of fibrous tissue and muscle that provides support for the pelvic floor muscles above, and it surrounds the anus and the urogenital passages. It is bounded in front by the pubic arch and the inferior pubic ligament, at the back by the tip of the coccyx, and at both sides by the inferior rami of the pubis and ischium and the sacrotuberous ligament.

In males, the urethra passes through the perineum to run along the penis. The perineum also contains the superficial and deep perineal pouches, fat-filled spaces on either side of the anus and rectum called the ischioanal (or ischiorectal) fossae, and the pudendal canal, which contains the internal pudendal artery and the pudendal nerve, which supply blood and innervation to the region.

inferior view

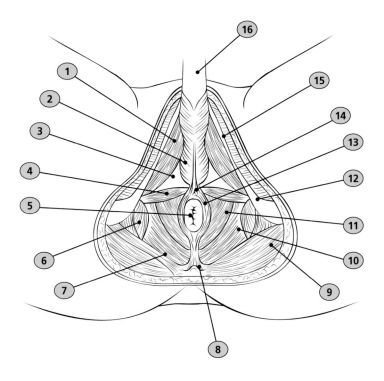

Muscles of the Perineum: Female

Key:

1 Ischiocavernosus
2 Bulbospongiosus
3 Vaginal opening
4 Superficial transversus perinei
5 External anal sphincter
6 Anus
7 Gluteus maximus
8 Coccyx
9 Iliococcygeus
10 Pubococcygeus
11 Deep transversus perinei
12 External urethral orifice

Description:

The perineum is a diamond-shaped "floor" at the base of the pelvis. It consists of a sheet of fibrous tissue and muscle that provides support for the pelvic floor muscles above, and it surrounds the anus and the urogenital passages. It is bounded in front by the pubic arch and the inferior pubic ligament, at the back by the tip of the coccyx, and at both sides by the inferior rami of the pubis and ischium and the sacrotuberous ligament.

In the female, the urethra passes through the perineum in front of the vagina, to open at the urethral orifice. The perineum also contains the superficial and deep perineal pouches, fat-filled spaces on either side of the anus and rectum called the ischioanal (or ischiorectal) fossae, and the pudendal canal, which contains the internal pudendal artery and the pudendal nerve, which supply blood and innervation to the region.

inferior view

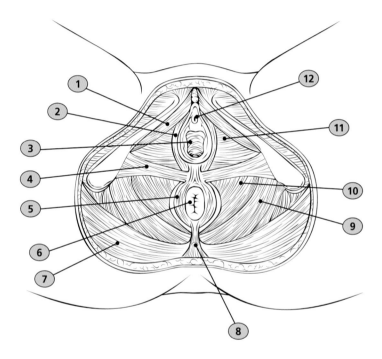

Superficial and Deep Muscles of the Shoulder

Key:

1 Pectoralis minor
2 Serratus anterior
3 Deltoid
4 Pectoralis major
5 Trapezius

Description:

The muscles associated with the shoulder and pectoral girdle fall into two groups—those attaching the humerus to the shoulder girdle and trunk wall, and those attaching the shoulder girdle to the trunk. As a general rule, the muscles that pass in front of the shoulder joint act to flex or medially (internally) rotate the humerus. Conversely, the muscles that pass behind the shoulder joint act to extend or laterally (externally) rotate the humerus.

The large deltoid muscle passes over three sides of the shoulder joint, and, as a result, it is involved in most shoulder movements. The deltoid muscle is important for abduction of the humerus, but anterior parts can produce flexion, and posterior parts contribute to extension of the humerus. The pectoralis major is a powerful adductor of the arm and a medial rotator of the humerus. Pectoralis minor acts to move the scapula forward, and elevates rib pairs 3–5 during forced inspiration when the scapula and humerus are fixed (for example when holding a chair). Serratus anterior is essential for scapular rotation and protraction.

anterior view

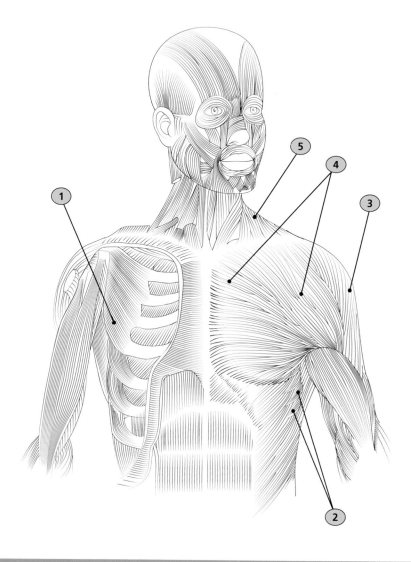

Superficial and Deep Muscles of the Shoulder

Key:

1 Trapezius
2 Deltoid
3 Latissimus dorsi
4 Infraspinatus
5 Rhomboid major
6 Rhomboid minor
7 Supraspinatus
8 Levator scapulae

Description:

The pectoral girdle has two groups of muscles—one group attaches the humerus to the shoulder girdle, and the other attaches the shoulder girdle to the trunk.

The trapezius plays a role in rotating the scapula upward, and the rhomboids are involved in downward rotation. The deltoid is involved in movements such as flexion, extension, abduction, and medial rotation. Latissimus dorsi is involved in extension, medial rotation, and adduction. Infraspinatus rotates the arm laterally, and supraspinatus assists the deltoid muscle in abducting the arm.

anterior view

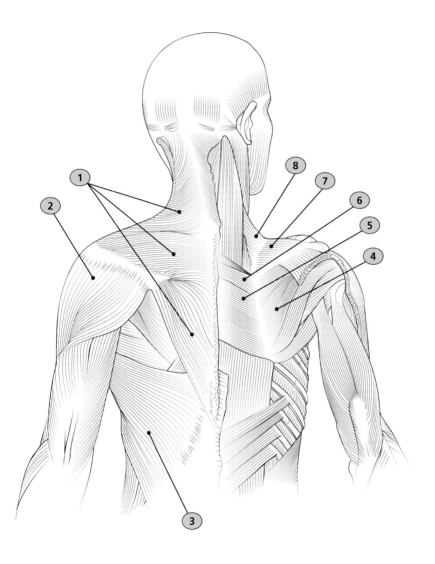

Superficial Muscles of the Upper Limb

Anterior View Key:

1 Pectoralis major
2 Triceps brachii
3 Pronator teres
4 Tendon of flexor carpi ulnaris
5 Flexor digitorum superficialis
6 Tendon of palmaris longus
7 Tendon of flexor carpi radialis
8 Brachioradialis
9 Brachialis
10 Biceps brachii
11 Deltoid

Posterior View Key:

12 Deltoid
13 Triceps brachii (long head)
14 Anconeus
15 Flexor carpi ulnaris
16 Extensor pollicis brevis
17 Abductor pollicis longus
18 Extensor digitorum
19 Extensor digiti minimi
20 Brachioradialis

Description:

The upper limb has three parts—the arm, the section between the shoulder and elbow; the forearm, which extends from the elbow to the wrist; and the hand.

At the shoulder, important muscles involved in movement include the deltoid, which makes the rounded contour over the upper surface of the arm and shoulder; the pectoralis major; the latissimus dorsi; and the teres major and minor. At the elbow joint, important muscles for flexion include biceps brachii and brachialis, while the main extensor is the triceps brachii. Most of the powerful muscles for gripping an object lie in the inside (front) of the forearm. The forearm extensor muscles, which are used for straightening the fingers, lie on the outside (back) of the forearm. The extensor digitorum and extensor digiti minimi extend the digits two to four, and five, respectively.

anterior view—left limb

posterior view—right limb

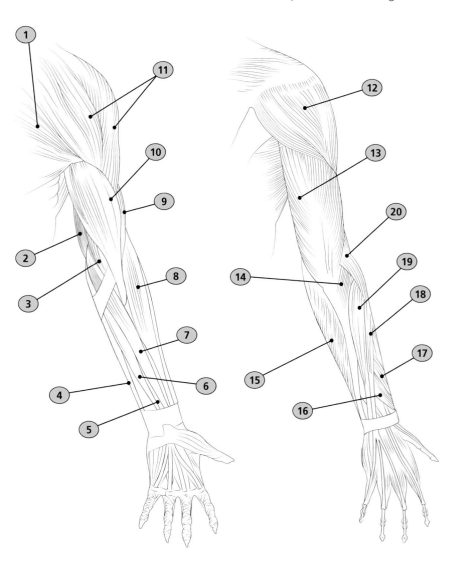

Deep Muscles of the Upper Limb

Anterior View Key:
1 Flexor digitorum profundus
2 Flexor pollicis longus
3 Supinator
4 Extensor carpi radialis longus
5 Biceps brachii

Posterior View Key:
6 Supraspinatus
7 Infraspinatus
8 Teres major
9 Supinator
10 Extensor pollicis longus
11 Extensor digitorum
12 Extensor indicis
13 Extensor pollicis brevis
14 Abductor pollicis longus
15 Triceps brachii
16 Teres minor

Description:

The upper limb extends from the shoulder, where it is attached to the trunk, to the wrist and hand. The upper limb contains powerful muscles involved in shoulder movement, elbow movement, and hand movements. Contributing to shoulder movement are the rotator cuff muscles—infraspinatus, supraspinatus, and teres minor, which are found at the posterior of the shoulder region, and subscapularis, which lies at the front.

The deep muscles of the arm and forearm contribute to the overall mobility of the limb. The flexor muscles, which provide a gripping action for the hand, lie in the front of the forearm. The flexor digitorum profundus is the deep flexor of the fingers while the flexor pollicis longus flexes the thumb. The supinator acts with the biceps brachii to supinate the forearm. The extensor carpi radialis longus extends and abducts the hand.

anterior view—left limb

posterior view—right limb

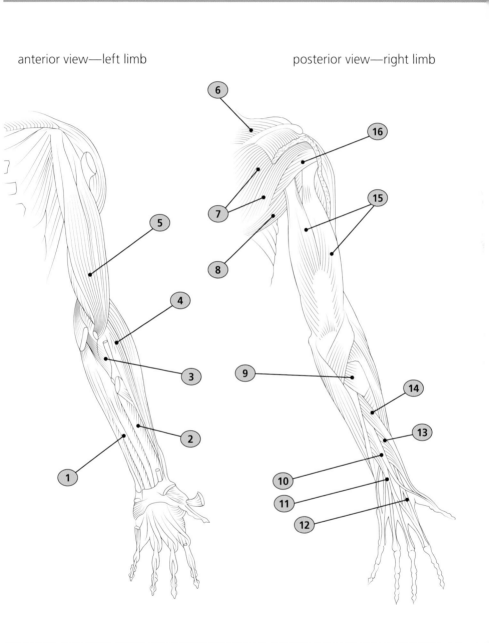

Muscles of the Arm

Key:

1 Biceps brachii
2 Brachialis
3 Humerus (shaft)
4 Triceps brachii (lateral head)
5 Triceps brachii (medial head)
6 Triceps brachii (long head)

Description:

The transverse section of the upper arm shows the position of the powerful muscles of the region. Encircling the humerus, the muscles of the upper arm provide a range of movements to the shoulder and elbow. The biceps brachii and brachialis produce flexion at the elbow, and the biceps brachii also produces supination of the hand. The triceps brachii is a powerful extensor of the elbow.

transverse section—left limb

anterior

lateral

medial

posterior

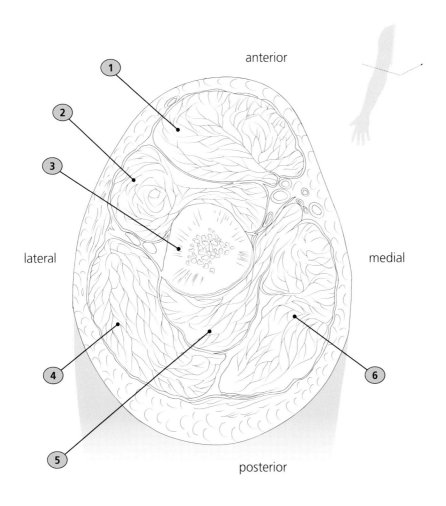

Muscles of the Elbow

Key:

1 Triceps brachii
2 Biceps brachii
3 Brachioradialis
4 Pronator teres
5 Flexor carpi radialis
6 Biceps brachii tendon
7 Palmaris longus

8 Flexor digitorum superficialis
9 Flexor carpi ulnaris
10 Brachialis tendon
11 Coronoid process
12 Trochlea
13 Common flexor tendons
14 Brachialis

Description:
The elbow joint separates the humerus of the arm from the forearm bones (the radius and ulna). This synovial hinge joint allows the forearm to flex and extend at the elbow. Important muscles for flexion include biceps brachii and brachialis, while the main extensor muscle is triceps brachii. The forearm muscles, extending from the elbow to the hand, allow rotation of the forearm (from supination to pronation and vice versa), flexion of the hand at the wrist, and flexion of the digits.

anterior view—right limb

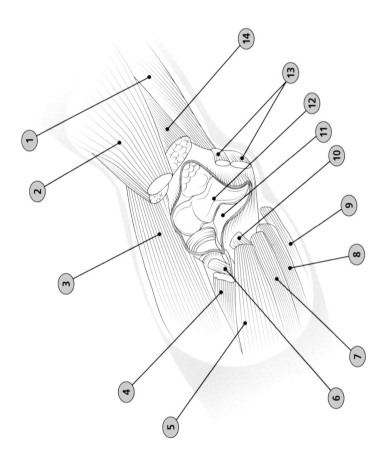

Muscles of the Elbow

Key:

1 Brachialis
2 Lateral epicondyle of
   humerus
3 Brachioradialis
4 Common extensor tendon
5 Radius
6 Ulna
7 Flexor digitorum superficialis

8 Flexor carpi ulnaris
9 Olecranon
10 Olecranon bursa
11 Medial epicondyle
12 Brachialis
13 Humerus
14 Triceps brachii

Description:
Connecting the humerus of the arm to the forearm bones of the radius and ulna, the elbow joint is a relatively stable synovial hinge joint that allows flexion and extension of the forearm. Located at the back of the arm is the muscle dedicated primarily to extension, the triceps brachii. The forearm muscles also contribute to rotation of the forearm, flexion of the hand at the wrist, and flexion of the digits.

posterior view—left limb

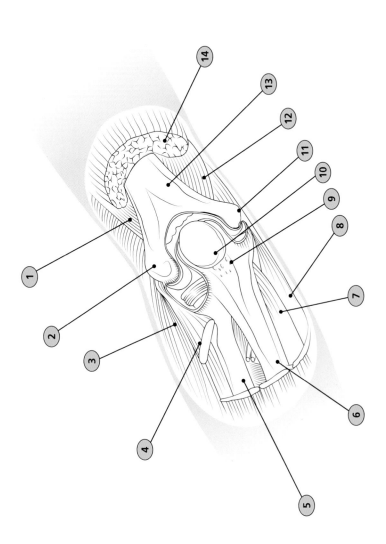

Muscles of the Wrist and Hand

Key:

1 Dorsal interosseous muscles
2 Extensor digiti minimi
3 Abductor pollicis longus
4 Extensor digitorum
5 Extensor pollicis brevis
6 Extensor pollicis longus
7 Extensor carpi radialis brevis
8 Extensor carpi radialis longus

Description:
The hand is designed to grasp and manipulate objects. The long tendons of the extensor muscles, associated with extension of the fingers and thumb, pass across the back of the wrist.

The dorsal interosseous muscles abduct the fingers, the extensor muscles are associated with straightening of the fingers and thumb, and the abductor pollicis longus abducts the thumb.

dorsal view—left limb

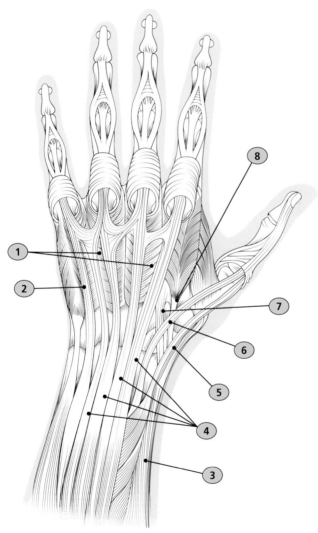

Muscles of the Wrist

Key:

1 Flexor retinaculum
2 Tendinous sheath of flexor digitorum superficialis
3 Flexor carpi radialis
4 Flexor digitorum superficialis tendons
5 Thenar muscles

Description:
Some of the muscles of the forearm converge at the wrist, with their tendons extending over the wrist area. These muscles contribute to movements of the hand. The long flexor tendons to the fingers and thumb pass over the front of the wrist through tendon sheaths, which are designed to protect the tendons and reduce friction as they pass over the carpal bones. The long tendons of the extensor muscles, associated with extension of the fingers and thumb, pass across the back of the wrist.

Flexor digitorum superficialis flexes the middle phalanx of the index, middle, ring, and little fingers. Flexor carpi radialis flexes and abducts the wrist.

palmar view—right limb

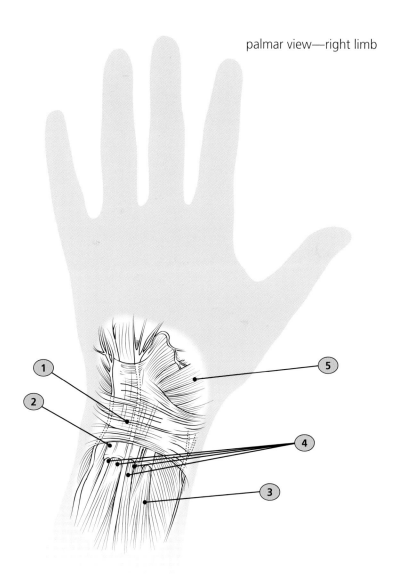

Superficial Muscles of the Lower Limb

Anterior View Key:
1 Tensor fasciae latae
2 Iliopsoas
3 Pectineus
4 Sartorius
5 Adductor longus
6 Vastus lateralis
7 Iliotibial tract
8 Fibularis longus (peroneus longus)
9 Extensor digitorum longus
10 Tibialis anterior
11 Soleus
12 Gastrocnemius, medial head
13 Vastus medialis
14 Rectus femoris
15 Gracilis

Posterior View Key:
16 Semimembranosus
17 Gracilis
18 Semitendinosus
19 Gracilis tendon
20 Soleus
21 Gastrocnemius, medial head
22 Gastrocnemius, lateral head
23 Biceps femoris
24 Gluteus maximus
25 Gluteus medius

Description:
The gluteal (buttock) region is dominated by gluteus maximus, which powerfully extends the thigh when running or climbing.

The quadriceps femoris muscle (rectus femoris, vastus lateralis, vastus medialis, and vastus intermedius) extends or straightens the knee, and the rectus femoris component also flexes the thigh on the pelvis. The hamstring muscles in the posterior compartment (semimembranosus, semitendinosus, and the long head of biceps femoris) extend the hip joint and flex the knee joint. Adductor muscles of the medial thigh make up the third group.

The anterior leg compartment contains the muscles that move the foot upward. The lateral compartment contains the fibularis longus and fibularis brevis muscles, which turn the sole of the foot outward (eversion). The third (posterior) compartment contains the gastrocnemius and soleus muscles.

anterior view—right limb

posterior view—right limb

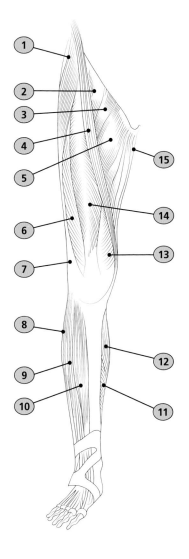

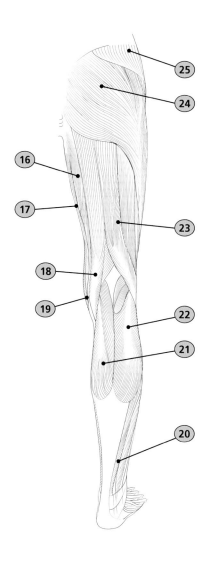

Deep Muscles of the Lower Limb

Anterior View Key:
1 Pectineus
2 Vastus lateralis
3 Vastus intermedius
4 Iliotibial tract (cut)
5 Tibialis anterior
6 Extensor hallucis longus
7 Rectus femoris (cut)
8 Adductor magnus
9 Adductor longus (cut)
10 Adductor brevis
11 Adductor longus (cut)
12 Sartorius (cut)

Posterior View Key:
13 Piriformis
14 Superior gemellus
15 Inferior gemellus
16 Quadratus femoris
17 Gracilis
18 Adductor magnus
19 Plantaris
20 Tibialis posterior
21 Flexor digitorum longus
22 Flexor hallucis longus
23 Fibularis longus (peroneus longus)
24 Popliteus

Description:
The deep muscles of the medial thigh include the adductor muscles—
adductor magnus, adductor longus, and adductor brevis—which lie
medial to the quadriceps femoris muscle. The adductor muscles act to
rotate, flex, and adduct the thigh and are important in counterbalancing
the action of the gluteus medius and gluteus minimus muscles (abductors
of the hip) when walking. The deep muscles of the anterior leg include
the extensor muscles—tibialis anterior, extensor hallucis longus and
extensor digitorum longus—which extend the foot at the ankle (dorsiflex
the ankle) and extend the toes.

The posterior compartment of the calf contains a deep group of
muscles. The largest of these, flexor hallucis longus, is critical for pushing
off from the big toe during walking. Other deep flexors bend the toes
(flexor digitorum) and invert the foot (tibialis posterior).

anterior view—right limb

posterior view—right limb

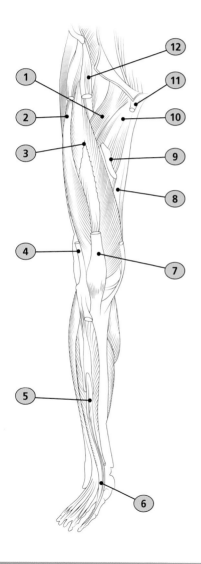

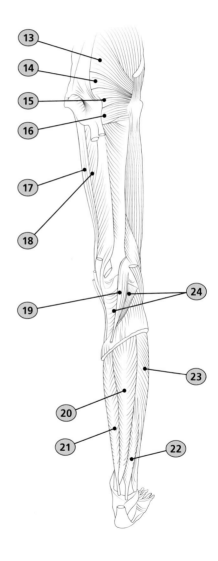

Muscles of the Thigh

Key:

1 Vastus lateralis
2 Vastus intermedius
3 Rectus femoris
4 Vastus medialis

Quadriceps femoris muscles

5 Adductor longus
6 Sartorius
7 Gracilis
8 Adductor magnus
9 Semimembranosus
10 Semitendinosus
11 Biceps femoris

Hamstring muscles

Description:

The transverse section shows the superficial and deep muscles found in the thigh region. The thigh contains the quadriceps, hamstring, and adductor muscles occupying the anterior, posterior, and medial compartments respectively. Nerves and vessels (femoral nerve, femoral artery, and femoral vein) lie in the fascial plane between the anterior and medial compartments.

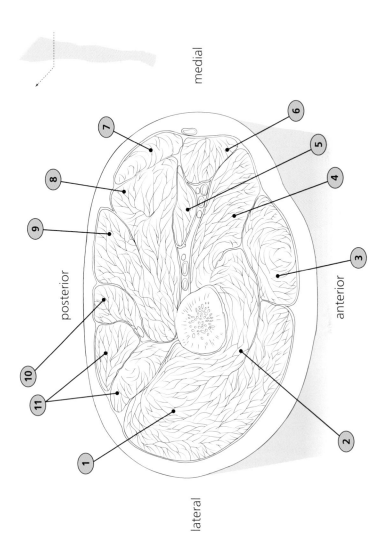

medial

lateral

posterior

anterior

transverse section—right limb

Muscles of the Foot

Key:

1 Achilles (calcaneal) tendon
2 Tendon sheaths
3 Superior fibular retinaculum
4 Inferior fibular retinaculum
5 Fibularis longus tendon
6 Extensor digitorum brevis
7 Fibularis brevis tendon
8 Fibularis tertius tendon
9 Extensor digitorum brevis tendons

10 Extensor hallucis longus tendon
11 Extensor digitorum longus tendons
12 Inferior extensor retinaculum
13 Extensor hallucis longus
14 Superior extensor retinaculum
15 Extensor digitorum longus
16 Tibialis anterior

Description:

The main muscles producing dorsiflexion of the foot arise at the front of the leg, while the main muscles producing plantarflexion arise at the back of the leg. Between the toes are the interosseous muscles, which act to adduct and abduct the toes. Fibularis longus and fibularis tertius are involved in plantarflexion and eversion of the foot, and fibularis longus also abducts the foot. The extensor muscles in the foot act to extend the toes.

lateral view—right limb

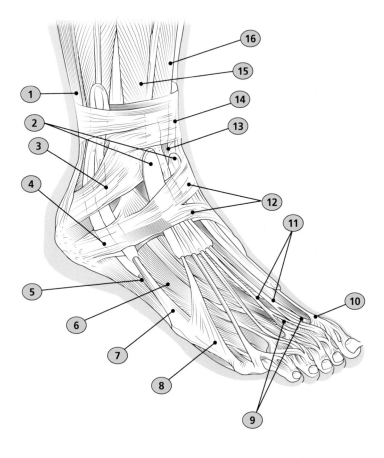

Muscles of the Foot

Key:

1 Tibialis posterior
2 Flexor digitorum longus
3 Tibia
4 Flexor digitorum longus tendon
5 Tibialis posterior tendon
6 Flexor retinaculum
7 First metatarsal
8 Calcaneal tuberosity
9 Achilles (calcaneal) tendon
10 Flexor hallucis longus tendon
11 Peroneus (or fibularis) longus tendon
12 Fibula
13 Peroneus (or fibularis) brevis tendon
14 Flexor hallucis longus

Description:

Many of the muscles of the leg converge at the ankle, narrow into tendons, and then extend across the front, back, and sides of the ankle. The tendons are anchored by flexor retinacula around the ankle. Tendon sheaths protect the tendons as they pass across the ankle joint. Lying at the back of the ankle is the Achilles (calcaneal) tendon.

Flexor hallucis longus flexes the big toe, while flexor digitorum longus flexes the remaining toes, and tibialis posterior and fibularis longus are involved in plantarflexion. Tibialis posterior also inverts the foot, while fibularis longus also everts and abducts the foot.

posteromedial view—right limb

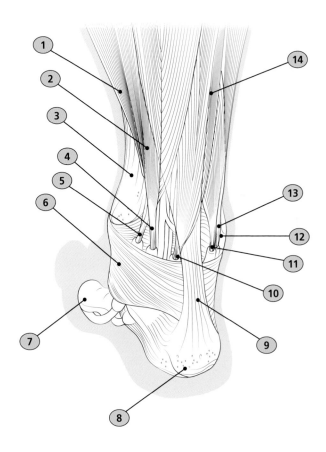

First and Second Layer Muscles of the Foot

Key:

1 Flexor digitorum brevis
2 Abductor hallucis
3 Abductor digiti minimi
4 Quadratus plantae
5 Lumbricals

Description:

Long tendons extend along the sole of the foot, which also contains a number of small muscles. These muscles are arranged in four layers. At a superficial level, the sole of the foot is dominated by flexor digitorum brevis, abductor hallucis, and abductor digiti minimi.

The flexor muscles found in the superficial layer of the sole of the foot act to flex the toes. Abductor hallucis flexes and abducts the big toe, while abductor digiti minimi abducts the little (fifth) toe. The thin lumbricals found in the second layer assist in joint movement between the metatarsal bones and the phalanges of the toes. Quadratus plantae assists the flexor muscles.

inferior view

first layer muscles

second layer muscles

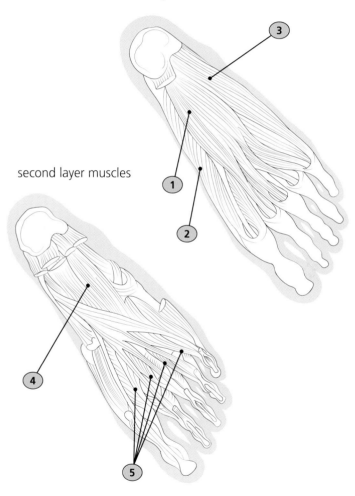

Third and Fourth Layer Muscles of the Foot

Key:

1 Flexor hallucis brevis
2 Adductor hallucis (oblique head)
3 Adductor hallucis (transverse head)
4 Flexor digiti minimi
5 Dorsal interossei
6 Plantar interossei

Description:

The third layer muscles of the foot comprise four muscles—flexor hallucis brevis, adductor hallucis (oblique head), adductor hallucis (transverse head), and flexor digiti minimi. They assist in the movement of the big toe and little toe, and support the arches.

Flexor hallucis brevis is a short muscle that flexes the big toe and supports the medial longitudinal arch. The oblique head of adductor hallucis adducts the big toe and supports the transverse arch, while the transverse head of adductor hallucis adducts the big toe. Flexor digiti minimi flexes the little toe. Located between the metatarsal bones, the fourth and deepest-layer muscles of the foot comprise four dorsal interossei and three plantar interossei. The four dorsal interossei abduct the toes and flex the metatarsophalangeal joints, while the three plantar interossei adduct the toes and flex the metatarsophalangeal joints.

inferior view

third layer muscles

fourth layer muscles

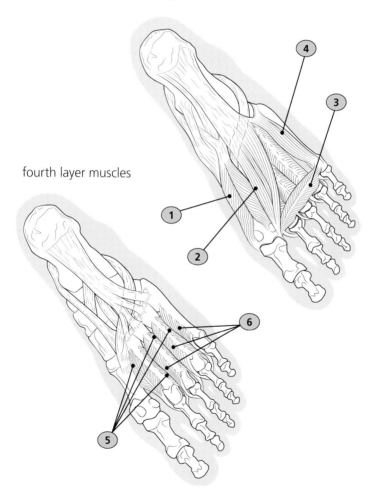

Digestive System

The digestive system is concerned with the ingestion of food and fluids, the breakdown of food substances into simpler molecules, the absorption of those molecules into the bloodstream and lymphatic fluids, and the excretion of waste products as feces. Essentially the gastrointestinal tract is a hollow tube extending from the mouth to the anus, with associated glands (salivary glands, liver, exocrine pancreas) and storage structures (gall bladder). The digestive system has its own nervous system (the enteric nervous system), which controls the glands and smooth muscle of the gut, but is also controlled by the vagus nerve from the brainstem.

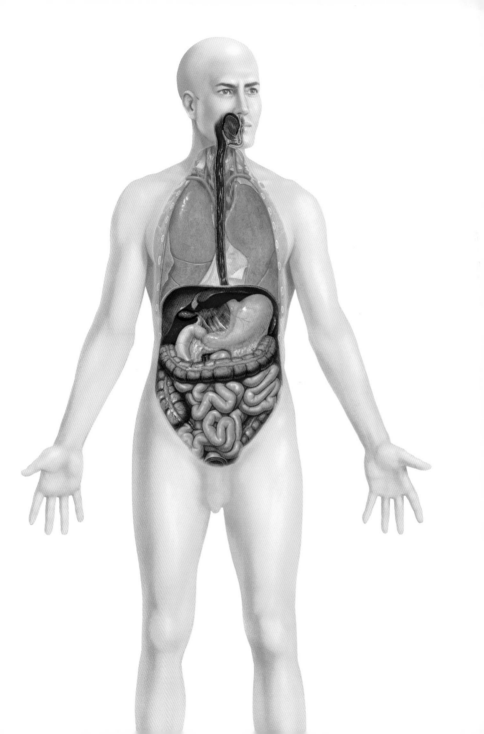

Digestive System

Key:

1 Tongue
2 Liver (lifted up)
3 Gallbladder
4 Duodenum
5 Pancreas (head)
6 Ascending colon
7 Cecum
8 Appendix
9 Rectum
10 Ileum
11 Sigmoid colon
12 Jejunum
13 Transverse colon
14 Spleen
15 Pylorus
16 Stomach
17 Gastroesophageal (cardioesophageal) junction
18 Esophagus

Description:

The digestive tract organs consist of the alimentary tract, which extends from the mouth to the anus, and the accessory organs of the salivary glands, liver, gallbladder, and pancreas. The mechanical action of the digestive tract optimizes the chemical actions of enzymes. The entire tract has smooth muscle fibers running in circular and longitudinal directions. The circular fibers contract sequentially along the tract (peristalsis) to knead the contents with digestive enzymes or to move digested food along the tract.

The process of digestion breaks down foods into small simple molecules for absorption as energy sources and building blocks for cells. Simple sugars, amino acids, and some small chain fatty acids pass through the portal blood to the liver for processing, whereas larger fat molecules pass through the lymph to reach the bloodstream.

anterior view

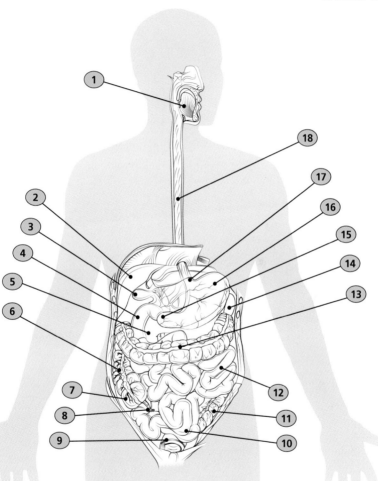

Oral Cavity

Key:

1 Hard palate
2 Incisors
3 Tongue
4 Trachea
5 Esophagus
6 Pharynx
7 Soft palate

Description:

The oral cavity includes the mouth and its associated structures —the soft and hard palates, the teeth and gums, the tongue, the palatine tonsils, and the salivary glands.

In the adult, thirty-two permanent teeth are arranged in two arcades of sixteen teeth each. On each side of each jaw are eight teeth—two incisors, one canine, two premolars, and three molars. The tongue is a muscular organ that is attached to the floor of the mouth and the back of the mandible. The tongue is divided into two main regions by the V-shaped groove of the terminal sulcus (sulcus terminalis). The front part consists of about two-thirds of the tongue and is covered with taste buds. The back third of the tongue is covered by the lymphoid tissue of the lingual tonsil, and also has taste buds. On each side, the tongue is joined to the palate by the palatoglossal arches, and immediately behind these arches are the palatine tonsils.

The principal salivary glands are the parotid, submandibular, and sublingual glands, which drain into the mouth through separate ducts. The parotid gland is located in front of the ear, whereas the submandibular and sublingual glands are located beneath the mandible and tongue, respectively.

sagittal view

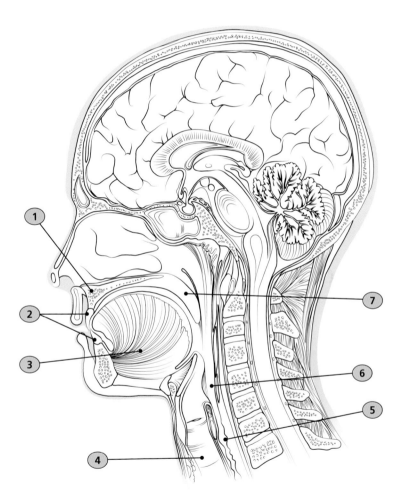

Digestive System

Tongue

Key:

1 Lingual tonsil
2 Palatopharyngeal arch and muscle
3 Palatine tonsil
4 Palatoglossal arch and muscle
5 Median sulcus
6 Fungiform papilla
7 Filiform papilla
8 Vallate papillae
9 Terminal sulcus

Description:

The bulk of the tongue is made up of muscle, which can be divided into two main groups—the intrinsic and extrinsic muscles. The intrinsic muscles lie within the tongue itself and are responsible for changing its shape. Their fibers are arranged vertically, longitudinally, and horizontally. The extrinsic muscles, which are attached to the jaw, skull, palate, and hyoid bones, are responsible for changing the position of the tongue.

The dorsum of the tongue is studded with papillae, of which there are three main types—filiform, fungiform, and vallate. Filiform papillae are tiny cone-shaped elevations that serve to grip food. Fungiform papillae are mushroom-shaped projections that may contain taste buds. About two-thirds of the way back from the tongue's tip lies a V-shaped group of 7–12 vallate papillae. These papillae have a central elevation that is surrounded by a deep groove. Taste buds are located in the groove. The pharyngeal part of the tongue behind the vallate papillae contains the lingual tonsil part of the tonsillar tissue ring that surrounds the entrance to the oropharynx.

Beneath the tongue lie the openings of the ducts from the sublingual and submandibular glands. The frenulum forms a midline ridge on the lower surface of the tongue.

superior view

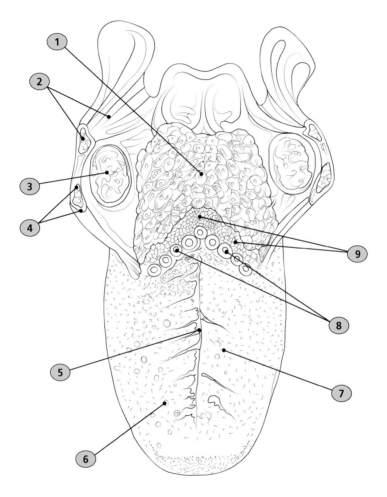

Teeth

Key:

1 Crown of tooth
2 Neck of tooth
3 Root of tooth
4 Alveolar vein
5 Alveolar artery
6 Alveolar nerve
7 Apical foramen
8 Alveolar process

9 Root canal
10 Cementum
11 Gingiva
12 Pulp cavity
13 Capillary plexus
14 Dentin
15 Enamel

Description:

Teeth are calcified bonelike structures in both jaws. The crown of a tooth—that part above the gum line—is covered with enamel, which is the hardest substance in the body. Under the enamel is dentin, slightly softer, which makes up the main part of the tooth. The dentin below the gum line is covered with cementum, a hard bony substance overlying the roots of the teeth. Dentin is a sensitive tissue, with millions of tubules running into the central pulp, containing the tooth vessels and nerve, which runs from the tip of the root into the center of the tooth. The cementum is surrounded by the periodontal ligament, which contains the tough collagenous fibers that anchor the tooth in the bone of the jaw.

longitudinal section

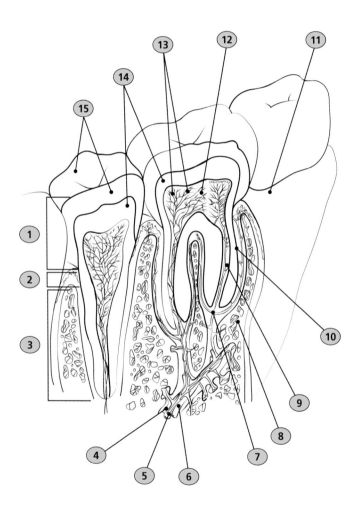

Oral Cavity and Salivary Glands

Key:
1 Sublingual folds (with openings of sublingual ducts)
2 Sublingual caruncle (with opening of submandibular duct)
3 Frenulum
4 Submandibular duct
5 Sublingual gland
6 Lingual nerve
7 Deep lingual artery
8 Deep lingual vein
9 Anterior lingual minor salivary gland

Description:
The underside of the tongue is soft and is kept moist by salivary gland secretions. The ducts of the submandibular gland open below the tongue, while the sublingual glands form a ridge on the floor of the mouth on each side of the tongue's base, and open by many shorter ducts into the oral cavity.

The frenulum forms a midline ridge on the lower surface of the tongue. Beneath and on either side of this ridge lie paired deep arteries and veins of the tongue, the veins of which are visible through the thin surface layer.

anterior view

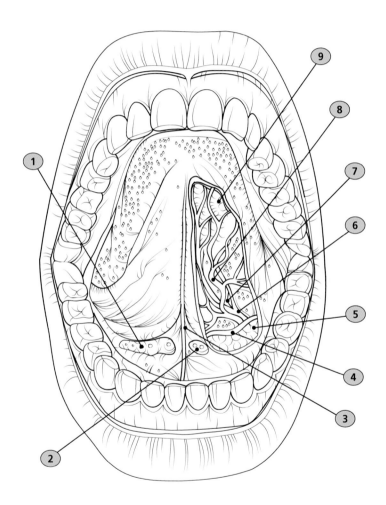

Salivary Glands

Key:

1 Accessory parotid gland
2 Parotid duct
3 Tongue
4 Frenulum
5 Sublingual gland

6 Submandibular gland
7 Facial vein
8 Internal jugular vein
9 Masseter muscle
10 Parotid gland

Description:

The salivary glands are located around the oral cavity and are divided into two groups. The major salivary glands consist of three pairs of glands—the parotid, submandibular, and sublingual glands. The minor buccal salivary glands are microscopic and scattered around the mouth, palate, and throat.

The parotid glands are located in front of each ear. They give rise to a duct that runs forward to open into the mouth, opposite the second molar of the upper teeth on each side. A flap of mucosa is present at the point where each duct opens into the mouth.

The submandibular glands are located below the jaw (mandible) on each side of the neck, about 1 inch (2–3 cm) in front of the angle of the jaw. They give rise to a duct that runs forward to open into the floor of the mouth on each side, under the tongue. The sublingual glands are small and lie within ridges on the floor of the mouth, beneath the tongue. They open by small ducts into the floor of the mouth.

Salivary glands are mostly under the control of the autonomic nervous system, and both divisions—the parasympathetic and sympathetic divisions—contribute nerves to the salivary glands.

lateral view

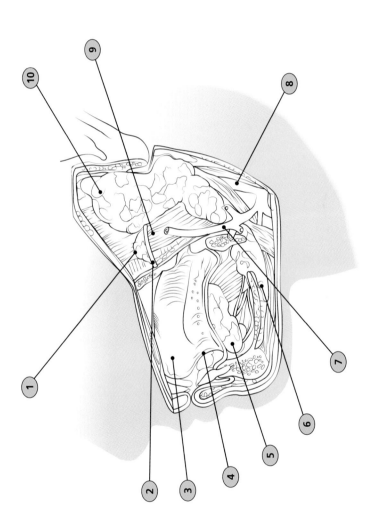

Digestive Organs and Greater Omentum in situ

Key:

1 Liver (right lobe, reflected up)
2 Gallbladder
3 Hepatic artery
4 Portal vein
5 Inferior vena cava
6 Duodenum (second part)
7 Ascending colon
8 Small intestine

9 Anus
10 Rectum
11 Sigmoid colon
12 Greater omentum
13 Abdominal aorta
14 Splenic artery
15 Left gastric artery
16 Liver (left lobe, reflected up)

Description:

Lining the abdominal cavity, and also extending out into the cavity to cover the organs within, is the thin lubricating membrane of the peritoneum. Folds of the peritoneum attach the organs to the back of the abdominal cavity, while allowing the intestines to move relatively freely to aid movement of food down the alimentary canal. Other folds of the peritoneum—the mesenteries and omenta—provide a route for the passage of nerves, blood vessels, and lymphatics to each organ. The greater omentum is a large apronlike peritoneal fold which is suspended from the greater curvature of the stomach and hangs in front of the small intestine. It has the ability to attach to, and isolate, sites of infection in the abdomen.

To identify internal organs and for diagnostic purposes, the abdomen is usually divided into four quadrants—right upper, right lower, left upper, and left lower.

anterior view

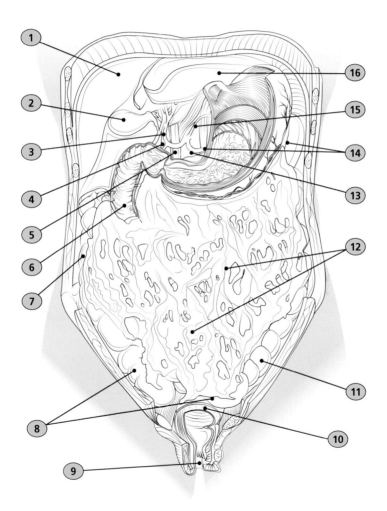

Digestive System

Upper Part of the Abdomen

Key:

1 Falciform ligament
2 Common bile duct
3 Portal vein
4 Cystic duct
5 Inferior vena cava
6 Liver (right lobe)
7 Right adrenal (suprarenal) gland
8 Right kidney
9 Right crus of diaphragm
10 Spinal cord
11 Vertebral body
12 Abdominal aorta
13 Left crus of diaphragm
14 Left kidney
15 Perirenal fat
16 Omental bursa (lesser sac)
17 Spleen
18 Stomach
19 Left gastric artery and vein
20 Lesser omentum (gastrohepatic ligament part)
21 Hepatic artery

Description:

Situated between the thorax and the pelvis, the abdomen is the larger of the body's three major cavities—the other two are the thorax, or chest, and the pelvis.

This inferior view of a transverse section through the upper part of the abdomen shows the relationship and location of the organs, structures, and blood vessels found in the left upper and right upper quadrants. Note the presence of the omental bursa behind the stomach. This is a recess of the peritoneal cavity that communicates with the greater part of the peritoneal cavity (greater sac) around the edge of the lesser omentum.

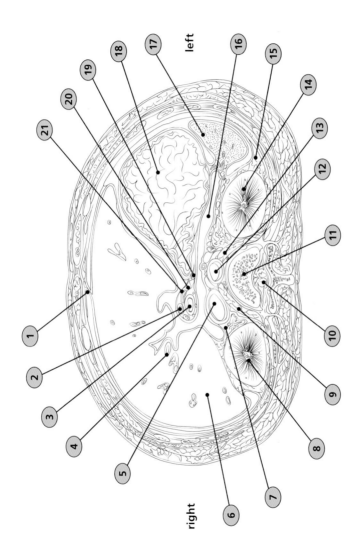

transverse section—inferior view

left

right

Middle Part of the Abdomen

Key:

1 Loops of small intestine
2 Ascending colon
3 Liver (right lobe)
4 Right kidney
5 Inferior vena cava
6 Spine of vertebra
7 Spinal cord

8 Body of vertebra
9 Abdominal aorta
10 Left kidney
11 Spleen
12 Descending colon
13 Transverse colon

Description:

The abdomen contains organs associated with digestion (the stomach, small and large intestines, liver, gallbladder, and pancreas) and urination (kidneys and ureters).

This inferior view of a transverse section through the midabdominal region—at approximately the level of the intervertebral disc between the second and third lumbar vertebrae—shows the relationship and location of the organs, structures, and blood vessels found here.

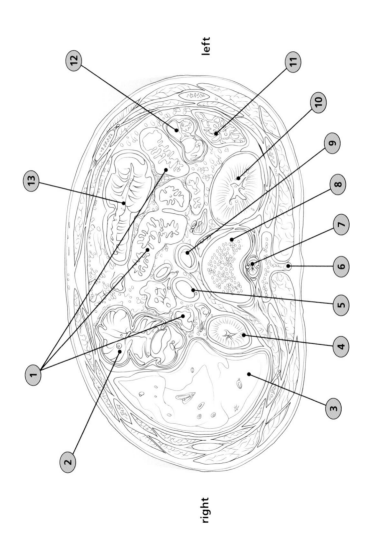

transverse section—inferior view

left

right

Liver

Key:

1 Coronary ligament
2 Liver (right lobe)
3 Anterior inferior border
4 Ligamentum teres
5 Falciform ligament
6 Liver (left lobe)

Description:

The liver is the heaviest internal organ in the body, weighing about 3½ pounds (1.5 kg) in an adult. Normally reddish brown in color, the liver lies under the cover and protection of the lower ribs on the right side of the abdomen.

The liver has an upper (diaphragmatic) surface and a lower (visceral) surface—separated at the front by a sharp inferior border.

The liver is attached to the diaphragm by the falciform, triangular, and coronary ligaments. The liver is also joined to the stomach and duodenum by the gastrohepatic and hepatoduodenal ligaments, respectively.

The visceral surface of the liver is in contact with the gallbladder, the right kidney, part of the duodenum, the esophagus, the stomach, and the hepatic flexure of the colon. The porta hepatis—the point where vessels and ducts enter and exit the liver—lies on the visceral surface.

The liver serves many metabolic functions. It plays a vital role in maintaining glucose levels in the blood, and also plays an important role in the metabolism of other sugars. The liver makes and stores vitamin A, and stores iron. The liver also produces bile and albumin, along with several important substances involved in the control of blood clotting, including the clotting factors prothrombin and fibrinogen.

anterior view

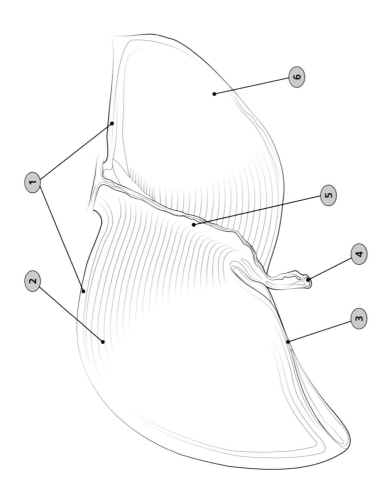

Liver Lobule

Key:
1 Hepatocyte plate
2 Hepatocyte
3 Central vein
4 Red blood cell
5 Hepatic artery branch
6 Portal vein branch
7 Sinusoid
8 Bile canaliculus

Description:
Microscopically, the liver contains sheets of cells (hepatocytes) arranged in hexagonal prism-shaped lobules. The space between the sheets of hepatocytes is filled with small blood vessels called liver sinusoids. Branches of both the portal vein and hepatic artery feed into these sinusoids, while a system of bile ductules runs between the hepatocytes. These ductules carry bile produced by the hepatocytes and eventually join together to form intrahepatic bile ducts, which in turn join together to form the bile duct. Bile is stored in the gallbladder and discharged into the second part of the duodenum in response to a fatty meal.

At the corners of each hexagonal liver lobule lie a branch of the portal vein, hepatic artery, and bile duct, while the center of each lobule is occupied by a central vein. The portal vein carries blood from the gut, whereas the central veins join together to form the hepatic veins that drain into the inferior vena cava.

microstructure

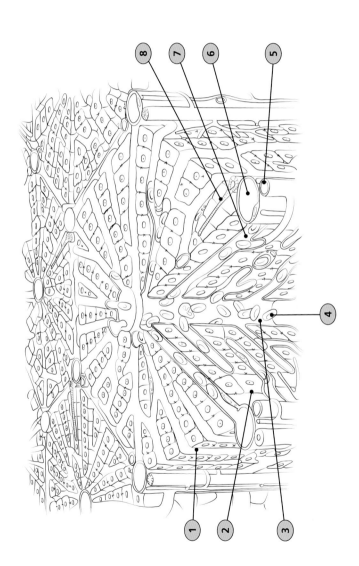

Gallbladder

Key:

1 Left hepatic duct
2 Right hepatic duct
3 Cystic artery
4 Fundus (of gallbladder)
5 Body (of gallbladder)
6 Neck (of gallbladder)
7 Cystic duct
8 Common hepatic duct

Description:

The gallbladder is a sac-shaped organ that is firmly attached to the lower surface of the liver and lies on the right side of the abdomen just below the ribs at the front.

The gallbladder is part of the biliary tree, a series of ducts that convey and store bile. Bile produced by the liver passes along the bile ducts and is stored and concentrated in the gallbladder. The gallbladder is joined by the cystic duct to the biliary ducts of the liver. The duct formed when the cystic duct and common hepatic ducts meet is called the common bile duct. The common bile duct passes behind the first part of the duodenum and down through the head of the pancreas to drain into the second part of the duodenum at the greater duodenal ampulla. Just before it enters the duodenum, the common bile duct is joined by the main duct of the pancreas.

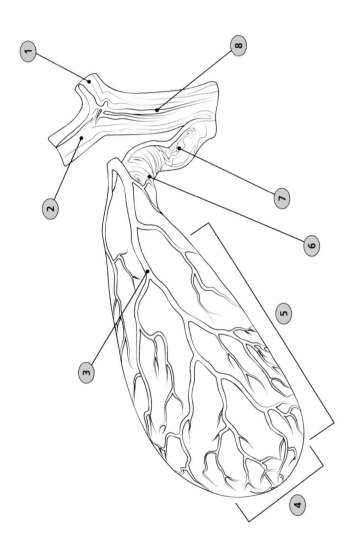

anterior view

Bile Ducts

Key:
1 Left and right hepatic ducts
2 Cystic duct
3 Gallbladder
4 Common bile duct

Description:
The bile ducts are also known as the biliary tree. The hepatic ducts carry bile from the liver to either the gallbladder for storage, or the duodenum for usage. The left and right hepatic ducts join with the cystic duct to form the common bile duct, which transports bile to the duodenum. The cystic duct transports bile from the gallbladder to the common bile duct.

anterior view

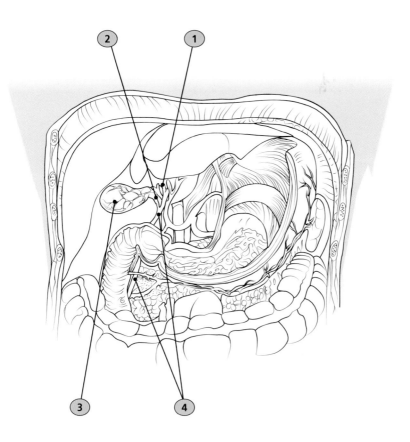

Portal System (digestive function)

Key:

1	Inferior vena cava	12	Sigmoid colon
2	Liver	13	Small intestine, jejunum
3	Portal vein	14	Descending colon
4	Duodenum (second part)	15	Left colic vein
5	Pancreaticoduodenal vein	16	Inferior mesenteric vein
6	Superior mesenteric vein	17	Pancreas (cut)
7	Ascending colon	18	Splenic vein
8	Right colic vein	19	Spleen
9	Appendicular vein	20	Left gastric vein
10	Cecum	21	Stomach
11	Rectum		

Description:

The portal system is the network of veins connecting the major components of the digestive tract to the liver. The primary veins in this network are the superior mesenteric, splenic, and inferior mesenteric veins. Blood draining from smaller veins throughout the tract is carried along the mesenteric and splenic veins to the portal vein, which forms behind the neck of the pancreas.

Also draining into the portal vein are the left gastric vein, which drains the upper part of the stomach and lower part of the esophagus, and the cystic veins that drain the gallbladder.

As part of the digestive process, nutrient-rich blood from the large and small intestines, the stomach, the spleen, the pancreas, and the gallbladder is carried along this portal system to the portal vein and then to the liver. Once processed by the liver, blood is returned to the heart via the inferior vena cava.

anterior view

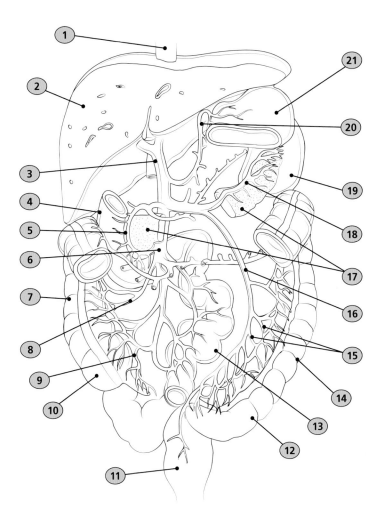

Pancreas (digestive function)

Key:

1 Tail (of pancreas)
2 Body (of pancreas)
3 Neck (of pancreas)
4 Head (of pancreas)
5 Accessory pancreatic duct
6 Uncinate process (of pancreas)
7 Main pancreatic duct

Description:

The pancreas is an elongated gland lying behind the stomach and in front of the aorta and inferior vena cava. The large head of the pancreas is framed by the C-shaped loop of the duodenum. Extending to the left from the head region are the neck, body, and tail of the pancreas, respectively. The tail meets the spleen on the left side of the abdomen.

Pancreatic secretions are collected by the main pancreatic duct, which, together with the bile duct, enters the duodenum at the major (greater) duodenal papilla, which is on the medial wall of the second part of the duodenum. Most of the digestive process takes place in the duodenum, due to the action of pancreatic enzymes secreted through the main and accessory ducts and the bile released from the bile duct.

The pancreas is a mixed gland and is a member of both the digestive and endocrine systems of the body.

anterior view

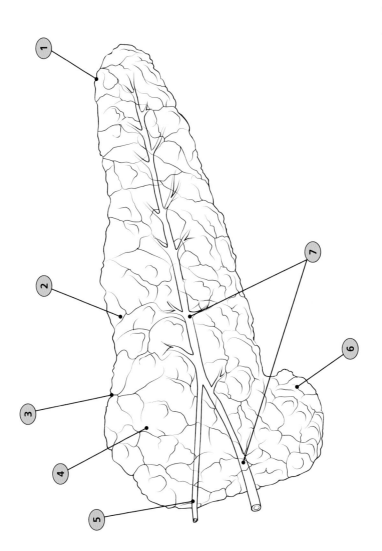

Stomach

Key:
1 Fundus (of stomach)
2 Cardia (gastroesophageal or cardioesophageal junction)
3 Pylorus (pyloric region)
4 Body (of stomach)

Description:
The stomach has a number of parts. The cardia is located at the entrance of the esophagus into the stomach (the gastroesophageal or cardioesophageal junction). The fundus lies to the left of the cardia, while the body of the stomach is the large central part that extends from the fundus to the pylorus. The pylorus is the final part of the stomach and consists of the pyloric antrum, which leads to the pyloric canal. The stomach has anterior and posterior surfaces, and greater (left) and lesser (right) curvatures. The greater curvature is the site of attachment of the greater omentum, whereas the lesser omentum joins the lesser curvature of the stomach to the liver.

The stomach receives food from the esophagus and continues the process of digestion. It acts as a reservoir and mixer. When empty of food, the stomach contains about $\frac{1}{10}$ pint (50 ml) of liquid, but can expand to accommodate up to 2.5 pints (1,200 ml). The stomach mixes food with acidic gastric juices and enzymes that digest protein and carbohydrates, before delivering semidigested food to the duodenum through the pyloric sphincter.

anterior view

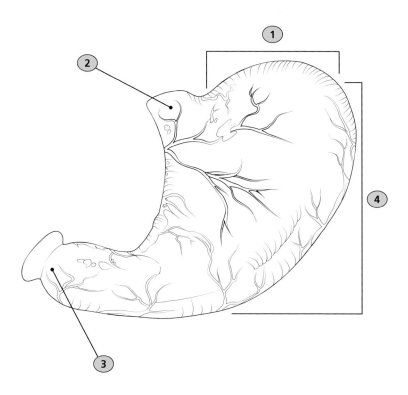

Stomach

Key:

1 Longitudinal muscle layer
2 Cardiac sphincter
3 Circular muscle layer
4 Submucosa
5 Lesser curvature
6 Duodenum (first part)

7 Pyloric sphincter
8 Pylorus (of stomach)
9 Mucosa
10 Greater curvature
11 Fundus (of stomach)

Description:

The stomach is a muscular organ, with the ability to churn and break down partially digested food into more easily digested fragments. The muscles of the stomach are activated in waves of muscular contraction (peristalsis) to move food from the body of the stomach to the pylorus. The pylorus is a cone-shaped gate of muscle between the stomach and the duodenum. When food is ready to be moved on down the digestive tract, peristaltic waves propel the food into the pyloric canal. The pyloric canal is encircled by the pyloric sphincter, a ring of smooth muscle that controls the passage of stomach juices and food into the duodenum.

The mucosa of the stomach contains a number of specialized cells, including mucous cells, which serve to protect the stomach from its own acidic juices; parietal (or oxyntic) cells that produce hydrochloric acid essential for digestion; and zymogen (or chief) cells that produce enzymes to digest protein.

internal structure

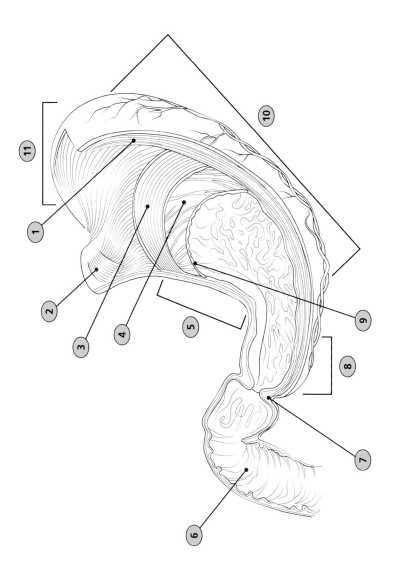

Stomach and Intestines

Key:

1 Duodenum
2 Transverse colon (reflected down)
3 Ascending colon
4 Cecum
5 Appendix
6 Rectum

7 Anus
8 Ileum
9 Sigmoid colon
10 Jejunum
11 Pylorus (of stomach)
12 Descending colon
13 Stomach

Description:

The stomach and small and large intestines are the principal organs involved in the breakdown and processing of food.

The intestines occupy the lower two-thirds of the abdominal cavity and consist of two parts—the small intestine (duodenum, jejunum, and ileum) and the large intestine (cecum, colon, and rectum). The small intestine leads on from the stomach, and the large intestine leads on from the small intestine. The large intestine is arranged like a picture frame around the margins of the abdomen and is composed of an initial part called the cecum, with the small vermiform appendix attached. It also includes the ascending colon, transverse colon, descending colon, sigmoid colon, and rectum.

The small intestine is mainly concerned with absorption of nutrients from food after digestion. The large intestine is concerned with absorption of water and salts.

anterior view

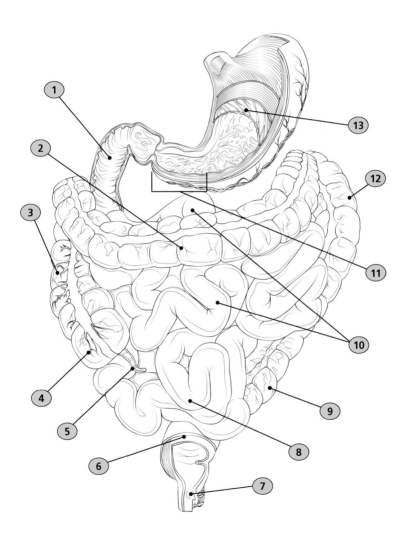

Jejunum

Key:

1 Serosa (mesothelium)
2 Serosa (connective tissue)
3 Plica circularis
4 Submucosa
5 Muscularis externa (outer longitudinal fibers)
6 Mucosa
7 Muscularis mucosae
8 Nerves of the mesenteric plexus
9 Muscularis externa (inner circular layer)
10 Villi
11 Mesentery

Description:

The jejunum, like the rest of the small intestine, is covered by smooth muscle, with an inner circular layer that is thicker than the outer longitudinal layer. The lining of the jejunum has many small transverse folds (plicae circulares) and tiny fingerlike projections called villi. The plicae circulares and villi greatly increase the surface area available for the absorption of nutrients.

The muscular layers of the jejunum, like the rest of the alimentary tract, generate wavelike contractions that move digested food along the tract. These muscular layers are controlled by the autonomic nervous system.

The small intestine is suspended in the abdomen by the mesentery, which attaches to the posterior abdominal wall. Blood vessels, nerves, and lymphatic channels lie between the layers of the mesentery, embedded in fat.

cross-sectional view

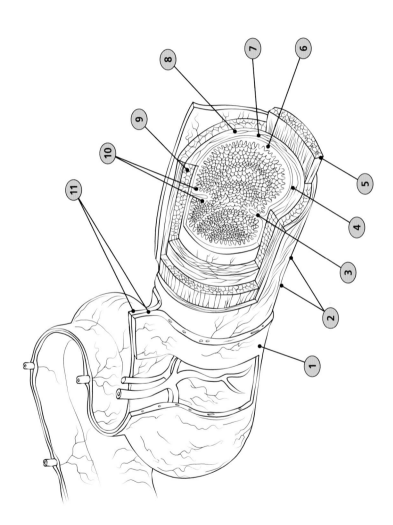

Intestinal Villus

Key:

1 Villus
2 Mucosa of small intestine
3 Circular layer of muscularis externa
4 Longitudinal layer of muscularis externa
5 Lamina propria
6 Basal lamina
7 Intestinal epithelium
8 Lymphatic lacteal
9 Lymphocytes

Description:

The plicae and villi on the lining of the duodenum and jejunum greatly increase the surface area available for the absorption of nutrients. The intestinal epithelial cells also have microvilli that contribute to this process.

Each villus has a rich vascular supply to allow the transport of amino acids, sugars, and small-chain fatty acids to the liver for processing. Lymphatic lacteals transport larger fats through the intestinal lymphatics to the thoracic duct and the systemic veins.

cross-sectional view

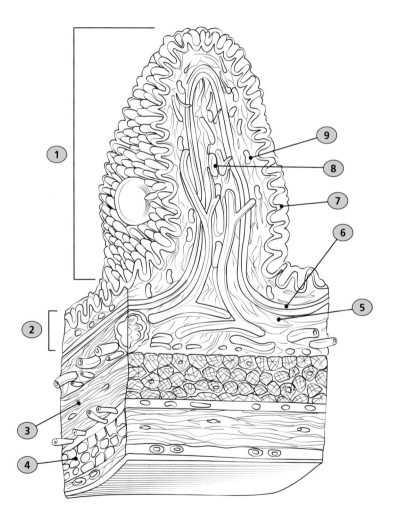

Rectum

Key:

1 Internal anal sphincter (sphincter ani internus)
2 External anal sphincter (sphincter ani externus)
3 Rectum
4 Sigmoid colon

Description:

The rectum is the second to last part of the digestive tract and leads to the last part, the anus. The rectum and anal canal measure 6–8 inches (15–20 cm) in length.

The upper part of the rectum has a series of folds in its walls called rectal valves. At the lower end of the rectum are longitudinally running folds called anal (or rectal) columns. The lower ends of these columns are joined together by anal valves to form the pectinate line. Immediately above each valve lies an anal sinus, into which open the anal glands. Below the pectinate line is the anal canal, which leads to the external environment. Sphincter muscles (the internal anal sphincter and the external anal sphincter) control the release of feces. The internal anal sphincter is continuous with the circular smooth muscle of the rectum and is involuntary. The external anal sphincter is striated muscle and is under voluntary control.

The rectum receives fecal material from the sigmoid colon and stores it for a short time until it is convenient to expel the stool. If feces remains in the upper rectum for prolonged periods it may become hard and dry and difficult to pass.

sagittal view

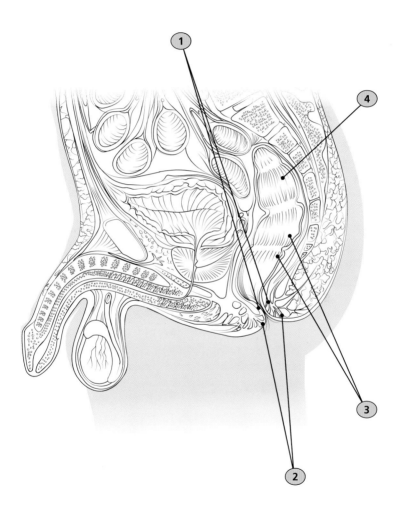

Anus

Key:

1 Rectum
2 Anal column
3 Anus
4 Anal valve
5 External anal sphincter (sphincter ani externus)
6 Internal anal sphincter (sphincter ani internus)

Description:

The anus is a short tube about 1½ inches (3–4 cm) long, leading from the rectum through the anal sphincter to the anal orifice, through which feces are expelled. The anus is closed by an involuntary and a voluntary anal sphincter—the internal anal sphincter and the external anal sphincter, respectively. The space on either side of the anal canal is the fat-filled ischiorectal (or ischioanal) fossa.

coronal view

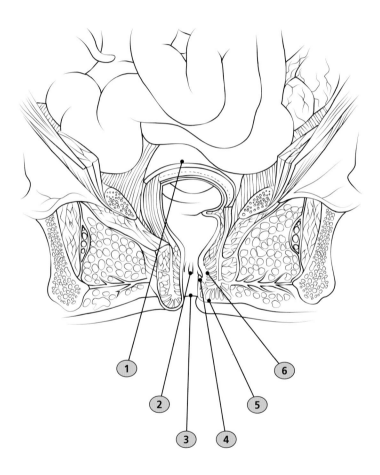

Index

Index